PRAISE FOR MORRY FRANK'S
EVERY YOUNG MAN'S DREAM

"Had F. Scott Fitzgerald's Jay Gatsby penned his own memoirs, what we may have encountered instead of Nick Carraway's version of an American Dream gone bad is Morry Frank's 'Every Young Man's Dream,' a stupendous work of a mature imagination."

George Stoya THE INDIANAPOLIS STAR

". . . 546 pages which at times will go by at a blistering pace . . . Darrel makes a great anti-hero for scholars."

Jim Ewing THE CLARION-LEDGER
JACKSON, MISSISSIPPI

". . . so fast paced and filled with realistic images that it is difficult to believe it is author Morry Frank's first novel."

Dennis O'Brien THE NEWS AMERICAN
BALTIMORE, MARYLAND

1

"Some writers are lucky that way. 'Every Young Man's Dream' is a fascinating exercise in expositional texture at its finest and the moral dilemma at its darkest and funniest extremes."

Mike Pearson SUNDAY HERALD TIMES
BLOOMINGTON, INDIANA

"First-novelist Frank goes at this naturalism as if trying to write Studs Lonigan all over again."

THE KIRKUS REVIEWS

"He has pounded out a literary dinger."

Mark Giles PEOPLE MAGAZINE

". . . a remarkable debut novel."

Jeff Nathan LOS ANGELES HERALD EXAMINER

". . . how rare it is to find a good baseball novel. How many can you name? We have a late entry: 'Every Young Man's Dream' by Morry Frank."

Bruce Cook LOS ANGELES DAILY NEWS

2

". . . pungent prose and images that as a sportswriter reviewing the book might say, grab the reader with all the tension of a no-hitter in the bottom of the ninth."

" . . . a cast of characters that would make Damon Runyon envious. The world is filled with Darrel Skaittses . . . who refuse to conform even though it means giving up their dream. In the end, Darrel Skaitts fails. But in his own way, he refused to compromise and that's not a bad epitaph for any of us."

"The best first-person novel I've read since Catcher in the Rye."

"My favorite sports novel of all time."

A LITTLE-KNOWN SAGA OF

THE LOST DAUPHIN AND YUKON KID

A NOVEL BY MORRY FRANK

SILVERBACK BOOKS
silverbackbooks@yahoo.com

silverbackbooks@yahoo.com

Copyright 2007 by Morry Frank

Library of Congress Catalog Card Number: 2007933156

Published by:
Silverback Books
Hollywood

ISBN 978-0-916747-18-3
ISBN 0-916747-18-2
silverbackbooks@gmail.com

Printed in U.S.A.

First printing March 2009

A LITTLE-KNOWN SAGA OF

THE LOST DAUPHIN
AND
YUKON KID

I am the Lost Dauphin, heir to the French throne. My blood goes back to Louis XVI of France and Marie Antoinette of Austria. It is proved through church papers in the Ministry of Haiti. Any petty official knew of me. I was not a secret.

From four to six years of age I lived with Granme and mama in a compound outside Port au Prince, refuged with other poor mulattos. Its center a dry cement wading pool with stone horses, I was at play there with two score children morn noon eve. At five with seniority I took it upon myself to lead. Older boys had escaped Haiti with their fathers.

While I played mama sat to a side watching. At this age I noticed how still she was compared to other mothers hearty of voice. She sat with a little pail wanting me to come eat which I was not wont to do. Abstemious by nature I sensed early on each bite should be counted, fresh air and exercise worth more and by exercise, play of a child or labor of an adult in carrying out his duties. Vainglorious exercise I have never done.

I turned five on a Sunday. Granme, who dealt with me from on high and never stooped, took a picture book from a valise showing me the Versailles with its grand foreground, horsemen and carriages traversing its cobblestone. Followed a great hall where King Queen with children sit for portrait, he stout rosy Louis XVI, she thin pale Marie Antoinette who came at twelve to marry him. The little boy is called Dauphin as were all to inherit the throne. In contrast the poor of Paris give ear to those against the king. Merchants tradesmen street vendors stand off, but as tax collections become heavier they must sell what they make for less, buy what they need for more and are drawn to rabblerousers, hearing them out.

Further the Kings' agents clad as street people report that criminals peasants laborers tradesmen are joined in riots. Marching on Versailles, Paris rabble turn so willful that the Palace Guard stand aside to give over the Royal Family. Their fate yet undecided, the King unsure as is his wont, the Queen meets with a handsome courtier who advises that she and King will face charges of treason and the Royal Family must flee the monarchy. Marie Antoinette and his court convince Louis of an escape, but the coach to spirit them away is not grand enough. Precious time taken to appoint it, they make a run for it in the night.

They have made twenty hours when an agent for rabblerouser Robespierre wonders why a coach with fine chests and horses is countryside this hour. He sounds a call and the coach is stopped ahead by militia. Though capable horsemen join Louis as escort he has them stand off and allows himself to be brought back to face trial in a hall of human vermin. He and then the Queen are sentenced for crimes against the People. Granme pointed to him standing before Robespierre. Because of his gluttony indecision pampering, she said, his people turned against him; the Queen too lost her head, the children their place and dignity.

Last pages showed Louis in blouse and cravat climbing scaffold, then Marie Antoinette in common frock skipping up thirteen steps with a smart tap of her heels to meet the blade to take her head, the executioner self-named Samson, who should ever be reviled twofold for his black work and for taking the name of the most noble of Hebrews. Last leaf, a harbor at an hour when even the blackest villain seeks slumber, a boy passes from courtier to corsairs, passage to the Americas assured by a pouch of jewels, the Dauphin, male of highest royal blood is saved.

Now Granme took out an old phonograph album, in the first envelope a copy of Royal Record, birth certificate of one Louis Charles Capet, meaning the Dauphin in the picture book. One certificate copy after another from envelope after envelope brought up what she knew about the decendant. Then came mama's, daughter of Granme and an American, Lee Overuse; then at last, *Daupin Louis Capet*, a tap on my head with it, bearer of highest French royal blood. A loftiness come over me that has not left, mama looked on with little idea whom she had born.

We stayed in this Eden until my sixth year. Is there better while for child than bucolic encampment with peers? But all Edens are brought to an end. Duvalier was ready for wholesale revenge on mulattos, giving his private militia, Tonton Macoutes, run to take what they could. To the rich first, of course, to us last, even the youngest in camp knew they were coming. They savaged Port au Prince splitting doors stripping homes stomping bloody anyone in their way, leaving little more than spattered walls. Some defecated before they left, like vultures on carrion.

Macoutes were a breed, lean field Negroes high of cheekbone, hue of damp earth, the worst of them faking hornrim glasses in tribute to healer turned torturer, Duvalier. Once they appeared, the two old Negroes at our gate depantsed and fled in their drawers. We watched them grow smaller as they climbed the hills. In berets, French jeans and American paratrooper boots, Macoutes marched in to impress mulatto women who I want to believe sickened at the sight of them. Leader of the small ones I stepped out arms wide and a Macoute in Duvalier glasses let go a kick that bounced me fifteen feet. Left leg cracked high at the shinbone, cords in the knee mangled, I was lucky the limb was not taken off. Haiti's doctors had fled the island leaving devious hospital orderlies – always opportune in crisis – to take office, some arranging to buy medical degrees. One such fiend set my leg so tight ringing went to my ears. I cried but Granme said it must stay. Mama who knew little, found an old jagged blade and dug the teeth into the plaster loosening it for me. This she understood with her little mind, saving my limb from lack of blood. When the cast was taken off, the leg was too bent to ever walk straight. As soon as I looked I knew it would not even to the right leg and I would be a cripple.

Before Macoutes came Granme was with much on her hands. Women came for skin and hair treatment she applied with balms she made up herself. She took only dollars in pay, no francs or Haitian, keeping wads in strips of cloth she tied to a canvas utility belt in support of her back.

When Macoutes came to our doorstep royal hauteur alone held these wolves from looking under her frock. The camp was so cleaned out that what money was left went for food. Granme got into an old cellar and commandeered a mess pot, cooking each day a bean okra broth she sold by the ladle for anything left of value. The same women came with bowls. Some cared for elderly mamas, and Granme took broth bedside because mulatto women were vainglorious chatterboxes devoid of patience to properly feed an elderly mama, shoving spoons in their mouths.

In both care of skin and hair and broth ladled out, they well got their money's worth yet resented all dollars in camp going to Granme, and we came back to the kitchenette one eve to find it turned over. No thieves had gotten over the gate. It was the work of women. Granme kept an eye on my progress and when I was hopping around our time in camp had come to end.

Holding a candle she woke mama and I. Two valises we took to the gate, met by a square little taxi. The driver secured them atop and us to Port au Prince where we finished night in a stone room with two cots. Morn we got on a bus to the Office of Visas where we stood and sat six hours before Granme came out bereft of most of the knots attached to her belt. A second night on cots, we went early to the harbor and boarded a tub to the Bahamas where we were encamped two weeks before coming over to America.

We were about forty days in a neighborhood south of Miami. Limping after Haitian children, thrilled by American toys, I remember my first word, *ride*, as I got in line to be pulled by a red wagon. We stayed in two rooms with an elderly man, a relative though I never did get the connection. Granme didn't go into explanation. A word or two she might give, followed by a look if I wanted more.

Granme got us clothing and matrons told her that once she was settled to take me to a county hospital and I would be fitted to a brace without charge. In our sixth week there Granme woke mama and I early Sunday. Valises packed full we were met by a man who drove us to the train station. We got on a Southern Chief, Granme Mama I sitting like everyone else. Many stops on way we came to Louisville, Kentucky, met by Granme's sister, *ma tante* had it mattered to her, a handsome woman like Granme, even taller. How hurried she was, her nose up. I followed her eyes yet she returned not a look. Her husband, chauffeur he was, drove us to a small white house at a curve of road, canopy around green as velvet. We were to have two rooms on one side. An elderly white woman, Mrs. Sperlock, lived alone on the other. I sensed we would be responsible for her else we would not have been so surely brought here.

Once the door closed behind us we were on our own. My great aunt did not come in. Granme didn't rest a day. Morn we walked downroad to a block of three story flats, knocking until Granme found a sewing machine at a good price. Then she did something I would not see her do again. She begged if there was a good gentleman who might drive us and the sewer back.

The machine was for night and weekend work under a lamp. Weekdays with mama in tow Granme took a bus downtown to care for two children for a young Jewish wife, arriving eight morn to feed and stroll them until four. To hear a compliment from Granme one could wait, but several times

I heard her say what a fine young woman Mrs. Robinson was, wife of a Federal official sent to Louisville. But she marveled at concessions given to two small children as to what they would eat and should or should not do. I'd never once bartered over anything she put in front of me or said.

Mama was good help because she loved to play with children, giving Granme leave to rest her legs. Granme took little from the American way except spaghetti. There is a difference in the nutritional requirements of Hispaniola and Kentucky. A bean rice meal suits a warm climate but the four seasons of Louisville make you a bread and noodles eater come fall; you feel you need it not to lose strength. Even with spaghetti she found her own way. There was nothing she did not do her way. For pennies she took shank bones from a market, boiled them clean, boiled them again in new water with spaghetti noodles and let them soak. No need for sauce sausages peppers, you ate a plate, all was good with you. The President of the United States would lick his lips. Granme ate a plate each day or, she said, felt a hole in her belly.

I stayed with Mrs. Sperlock daytime helping her to and from privy, sweeping floor, cleaning breakfast and noon meal dishes. This I did two weeks when on a Monday morn Granme gave me a packet tied with string and a word to bring it back the same way. Downroad I went to the three story flats following chattering boys and girls to a red brick school. Looking lost I was taken to the office. School secretary took the packet and sat me on a bench. I had picked up a little English and listened to her talking about getting married that coming Saturday.

She led me to a schoolroom to a tall white woman who sat me at an empty desk. I spoke little to her questions and she shook her head as though she didn't know what she would do with me. She was cold unfriendly and I saw my classmates were indifferent of her.

I understood little instruction but liked being with thirty my age, having my own desk pencil books, having writing paper passed to me, lining up for a tray with a slice of meatloaf, lump of mash potatoes, servings of succotash and fruit cocktail. It lacked strong flavors of Granme's cooking but I ate hearty like others and washed it down with milk.

When class read aloud I took what I could from pictures in the story. Learning alphabet from class recitation I began to sense letters blend in sight sound. I became intrigued by words recognizing them on signs and sides of buildings.

Numbers were not hard for me. Granme had taken time to sit with me to add subtract American coins she put on the table. I walked about wistfully adding up two quarters three nickels four pennies and such combinations.

On the playground I kept up best. The boys used to roughhousing with older brothers sisters could at age six flip one another over the shoulder in the way of Crash Corrigan Monte Montana Ken Maynard on old Saturday morning westerns they went to see for a quarter at the Coronet, learning from them American ethics of standing ground and protecting who are weak. Tagging along for this roughhousing, not oft left behind, I was tossed flipped slammed, learning to tuck my lame leg and hit flat to ground. Strongheaded I did not dizzy. In short time I hit with a thud I hardly felt and popped right back up.

I used speed for safety, my game leg a rudder to change directions, three evasions usually ending a chase, a squirrel's gift to out-turn out-slither out-skid my persuers. My right quarter grew round like the haunch of a kangaroo. My right arm outgrew the left. On that side I held my own. Notions of what I might do on two legs I let go – what use what could not be? Teasing older girls on the playground I turned and fled with the rest, walloped from behind but oft getting away. After school I wished I could have joined in more mischiefs but I had responsibilities.

Knocking on Mrs. Sperlock's door before letting myself in I stepped on a footstool, rinsed dishes cups spoons, then swept floor and peeled a potato that Granme would boil for supper and serve to her with sour cream.

At a nod from Mrs. Sperlock I went round to our side and peeled four potatoes eight carrots, and put them in a pot with buckwheat to simmer overnight for our breakfast. I went through childhood without seeing an egg pancake waffle yet believe I ate as hearty morn as anyone.

After rinsing Granme's mama's aprons – mama had to wear everything she did – I turned on the radio on the window ledge to the old teenager music and sat out on the side steps listening to Brenda Lee Connie Francis Fats Domino Jackie Wilson, waiting for Granme mama to return. So taken was I as Phil Diamond sang *Sea of Love* I rose as though it came down from the heavens. Singing to myself I learned to speak English with a little tune in my sentences. By the time school let out I was reading stories and went about managing coins in my head the way other boys dream of bicycles and flashlights.

First day school vacation I woke with Granme mama as usual, leaving in different directions. By now Granme had a lay of the land and told me to go opposite, round a curve of railroad tracks to two blocks of apartments called the Pensions and go door to door asking to wash dishes and run errands for a quarter.

I walked wide of tracks along shanties put up on blocks. It was open ground for the poorest around there. When I got to the Pensions I did not gaze about but went up the first stoop to the first door. Speaking to an elderly lady with pigtails as silver as a spoon I asked if she had dishes to wash or an errand I could run for a quarter. She stood a footstool at her sink holding a pot that soaked. I rolled up a sleeve, took a wire pad, scrubbed for all I was worth, rinsing but once to check for spots. Taking a bag of garbage out back, I was given a sack and food stamps and sent to a grocery on the next corner.

She took me out on the stoop pointing to one of two. I showed the grocery lady the list and she took the sack and deposited a bag of flour bottle of buttermilk carton of lard. Reading labels on all three I carried them back to Mrs. Dunn who gave a quarter, said to come again and she would have something for me to do.

Knocking on the next three doors, I went up a flight answered at the first. It was numbers work, I saw: make yourself available opportunity comes your way a little luck to follow. Bad fortune finds you even if you hide from the world under a bed.

For an elderly lady who didn't look like she could help herself much longer I washed dishes swept took out garbage. As I did this small work she cupped a hand under her chin with a finger over her mouth. Giving a quarter she looked in her refrigerator and asked me to come morrow to go to the store.

Next building a woman light as a mulatto but with thick features had me sweep mop. I thought that was about it but she produced a crusty grill I scrubbed with steel wool until my fingertips were raw. It took a half hour until it looked good enough to her. Then she played with nickels pennies until she finally got out a quarter.

After her I knew I would have to build up a clientele of nice old ladies who would not take advantage. Two more answered on the second floor, neither good. The first had me rub soapy laundry on a washboard, the other sand a rail on her porch. My fingertips cracked.

Finishing the day with five quarters I wondered if I could have made more by not announcing my fee, letting them pay what the work was worth. I suspected, though, that the grill lady washboard lady back porch lady would have given a dime. People without heart will work you all day, pay little or nothing and feel better for it.

Back along the tracks I saw a face I knew, Rollo, the outcast of Jefferson School. I was nearly the shortest in my grade and he came to my chin. His forehead lobes curved like a baby's buttocks and from a flat nose he liked to let fly on school yard to the disgust of everyone. To look at him was to think he was going to be a big midget or circus performer. He had no home training and could not sit quietly in class or cafeteria or play safely on yard. He brought no lunch money, pestered others for food and walked off without thanks. If someone brought a new gadget he was first pawing at it. He did not respect assigned play areas, roaming about for trouble, and was several times trounced by rugged boys in my class for interfering in our games.

Standing by was his brother Robert who I heard was even worse. Not getting his way in kindergarten he squatted in a corner and made a movement in his pants. Both had cigar-box shoeshine kits. Who they expected to come along scorched cinder for a shine I had no idea?

I looked like all the world to them.

'Shine your shoes for a nickel,' Rollo said, his nose tickling.

His brother saw I was scared, saying so. Rollo pointed to the Pensions.

'Been to yo Granma, get some candy money?'

At my silence he pawed my pockets. I would have run but Robert took a shoe cream bottle from his box, slapping it in hand like a sap. Rollo's fingers dug into my right pocket. I wore loose pants as cast-offs usually are. Up came the quarters. At sight of them his brother climbed over his back. Rollo bucked him off, looked skyward and honked through his nose like to geese up high. He'd missed the house key in the same pocket. It was jagged and had clawed into a corner.

He staggered off as though his life was changed, Robert pouncing after him. I went on key in hand. Without it I couldn't have gotten in to Mrs. Sperlock and would have been in a fix. Spared the key I was able to rinse her few dishes, sweep, and peel a potato.

Finished there I did my chores, peeling potatoes carrots, rinsing two aprons, sweeping mopping. Slumped on the stoop I wanted to tell Granme I found no work but the moment she put down her straw bag she determined something was not right. I told her I made five quarters but was held up by two boys from school.

'How old are these boys?' she wanted.

'One is my grade, his brother kindergarten.'

She opened her bag and took out a hardened bull deek with a rubber bicycle grip glued onto one end, the other end tipped with glue to create a loop when swung. Polish mercenaries come to Haiti with Napoleon's army used such as saps on Haitian heads. One of my early memories was seeing Granme take hers out and drive away a pawing tramp she later denied doing although I am absolutely sure I saw it. Hers a foot and a half, named *dybuk* its ridges swirled like rows of blunt teeth, its blow not so much whack as bite. Swung good it whined.

'You will not be your forebear – as he Queen children fled, they had ridden long hours, coming to a dunghole to change horses, not much longer to reach safety, when a snoop's call summoned rubes with farm tools. Joined by an escort of one hundred horsemen ready to cut a way through, this Louis, huntsman who could shoot seventy animals midday for exercise, was loath to fight, and for his effeminacy he and family were returned, confined to a tower, debased at the hands of rabble, separated from one another until he and Queen climbed scaffold to have their heads removed for the sea of *republique* gathered round – all because of cowardly constipation at shedding blood.'

21

She would have no male in house she vowed, who would not employ violence. 'Who will not fight when it is called for deserves neither wife nor child – no matter his station.'

She handed me dybuk. 'You will not let them take your wages again, not those two. Bring down on their heads, lay on until they are no longer before you. You will not stop until they are prostrate or escaped.'

Morn I took it in a wrinkled bag. I had not yet struck anyone but had the energy of two and was hard in ribs and backside from being slammed about by classmates. As for Robert and the shoe cream bottle, I advised myself dybuk must fly faster to his head than the bottle to mine. Reducing it to that I feared no less. Along the shantytown I expected they would come at me any minute. All clear I went to my first client, Mrs. Dunn, who showed me a stain ring on her tub on so hard it was plaque. I would not give in, rubbing it out by half. She squeezed my shoulder and gave a quarter, telling me to go to Apartment 3, a door I'd knocked on yesterday.

A frail woman, a pity really, gave a list and food stamps and sent me to the corner grocery across the street from the one I went to for Mrs. Dunn. A stocky man in bloody apron got a sack of sugar and string of wieners, then took a round cut from the meat case and stuffed it in a grinder, telling me to watch as he collected it in a paper dish and wrapped it up. On my return with these items she asked if I'd watched the Jewish man grind the round steak. I sat down at the table and she spread bread with butter and jam. I ate and she sent me down the hall to an elderly man who had me take everything out of a pantry, put it all on his table, wipe the shelves and put it back. It took twenty minutes and he paid a quarter and dime.

I went upstairs to my second client yesterday and was sent to a third store two blocks down. Returned with the items I took a bag of garbage out to cinder alley where I saw a long

22

box with burned out light tubes two feet in length. Hopping around I swung one side to side.

With five quarters and a dime it was time to go. A notion took me back to the alley. Sliding a tube under my belt aside like a swordsman, I mumbled childish prayer not to meet Rollo on the way back but it was simple of me. The way he honked through his nose at the sight of five quarters he had never beheld money like that. It was his biggest take until then and I was sure he would remember it all his life.

He and Robert waited with a long boy straddling a bicycle. Come closer it looked to me he didn't have all his marbles. Legs slowing, my heart quickened.

'Wutch you got?' Rollo called.

I drew dybuk out of bag.

'What's *that?*'

'Ol' pee dick.' I used bathroom talk of Jefferson School.

'Ol' pee dick?' he scratched his head. 'Who got a pee dick that long? You sit down, it drop in water and drown.'

His brother and the other boy giggled. To amuse more I said it was from a bull.

'Let me see!'

His lobed forehead bumping my chin, my nostrils quaffed his poverty. Holding dybuk back out of reach until he weighed on my chest, I pined *'Now! Now it must fly!'* and with little space swung down on his head with both hands. Batting his eyes he bent away. I hopped to smacking the back of his neck. In haste dybuk flew from my hands. Robert fumbled in his cigar box.

'Get him, *Robert!*' Rollo wailed.

He came waving the shoe cream bottle. I drew out the tube, poking it forth, coaxing him back.

'Wutch you waitin' for, Christmas?' pained Rollo. "Get his ass!'

His ears tucked between his shoulders he scampered to. Hands together overhead I shattered the tube over his skull.

Asmoke with ash, vapor curled over his ears. The friend on the bicycle tucked in his chin and pedaled away.

What was left of neon tube was stalactite. Rollo ran in fright, Robert chasing him, fleeing like from a truant officer.

Since that day I have done what most men do and I have done what most men would not chance, but there is no exhilaration as that from which you see your enemies flee before you.

In time I formed a clientele who needed little more of me than a cleanup and walk to the store which I liked to do best of all. I went to both groceries on the near corner and to one one over. Each of my clients favored a grocer. No Negroes owned these corner groceries. A rolypoly in goatee, beret and artist's waistcoat operated in the middle of the second block selling milk sodas smokes frankfurters in links. Little more than cubbyhole under stairs, army canvas for walls, he did well there, always quick to welcome with a spirited remark. It seemed well-to-do Negroes with property would get the idea to invest in a man of such personality, but he was in that hovel when I left Louisville years later. I stopped by as a grown man.

The corner grocers spoke thick English. They did not wear light color clothing and straw boaters like summer Louisvillians but dark trousers sweaters even when it seemed they would choose to stay cooler. My clients spoke of a Jewish man a Lebanese man a Greek; to me one seemed hardly other than another.

I was on my way 2:30 to my chores and listen to the old teenager music. Days were identical but what sunshine to put five six quarters in the jar on the table. Sometimes I held back a dime to give mama who loved coins and hid them away. After I'd given a few I became curious as to where she put them and looked everywhere.

I was raised like a girl not a boy. I looked forward to little, set hopes on not much but it was not monotony. I felt neither childish sadness nor joy but pleased at moving along. Eve mama I played checkers then listened to radio dramas that had come to their last days. Mama didn't know the words but thrilled at voices of public enemies and of hardy heroes who stood in their way. When she was in her nightdress I went out under the stoop to make like those voices and she would cuddle herself and whinny with her hands under her chin.

On Sunday Granme took us to a Christian Unity. She went not to pray but to pick up news as to what was available in government benefits and medical care. I liked going because I sensed there is God and liked to sing to Him as mama beside me sang along.

Summer done I told the Pensions ladies I would be back June. They would miss me they all said. It was time to go back to school where they looked after you and saw you got your lunch and milk and checked your teeth and lined you up for shots as we looked for who was brave and who was scared.

Once school started Granme took me on a Saturday to a clinic. A technition calibrated a brace to my leg. Next Saturday we went downtown to a medical building where I was fitted with a two-leather hold and brown shoes, the left with a round packer toe and built up sole and heel. Sharpness down to my toes was welcome in hope the leg would straighten . . . would it only come to three-fifths of the other.

I was in a room with most of my class from the year before. Our teacher, a round clownish man in old brown suits and painted cravats, would start instruction then stop to talk about his worthless relatives. His words spraying boys in front, they bent around with one eye shut until we were all laughing. I'd have rather been in class with them than anywhere else in the world.

In April Mrs. Sperlock passed on. Her son sat down at our table wanting more rent. Granme counting it out I read her face we would be there not much longer. Four weeks on, Sunday morn, we didn't dress for Unity. A man came and took the sewing machine, valises, household items we'd accumulated and drove us to a trailer van on high groundwork in shallow gully at curve of road. Across a field stood government projects three rows back.

Monday I was in a new school, my classmates from projects where they lived with mothers but no fathers. My former classmates were from brick flats run by grandmothers who gave orders and stout grandfathers who backed them up with a thick belt. Mothers had little say. Boys in my new class knew only to belittle and at the slightest provocation stood to fight. One had a father and granpa in the same penitentiary and was likely to make three. Our teacher didn't bother with us. He passed out paper and told us to copy pages of reading text. Those without were handed any book at all. In those six weeks before summer vacation I was regularly punched kicked. That I got through without injury I am yet amazed. I returned to the gully each day thankful I was whole.

School out for summer Granme mama and I took a yardstick behind the trailer and squared off thirty feet by thirty. I took a spade from the shed and turned over grass, exposing maroon Kentucky soil I scraped flat.

Next morn we rode a bus to a grocery that sold dry goods from burlap sacks. In the greenhouse in back a Caribbean man put 72 seedlings in the compartments of three beer boxes. Bringing them home we marked off rows to screw the mouth of a soda bottle into moist soil to place each seedling. Mama I nursed them with Granme having a look now and then. Returned from the Pensions I gave each a drink of water and plumped up the soil around it.

Always wanting to add a little extra to everything I did, I scraped up pigeon droppings, using old music show posters I tore from poles. Bringing home I dug up a little by each plant and put in a few pellets. Peppers grown bright red we filled six bushels and sold them at the side of the road to mostly older Negroes.

Our enterprise grew under tree canopy with an old rabbit hutch with wire cages as wide as a tall man's reach. A farmer brought white mother rabbits and babies for us to bring through. Mama and I fed watered cuddled kissed the little ones for seven weeks, and when the farmer came for them on a Saturday morn I suspected that by Sunday noon they would be bones on a plate. He brought more does, baby rabbits, a bag of pellets. I asked Granme if instead we could grow more peppers but she said there were not enough customers.

I now saw Granme as one who tolerated men only when she needed one; and for this type of woman a man will show up. Ol' Mud pulled up in an old hearse. If it was arranged I never knew. Immediately he was nailing up support for the hutch. What needed fixing, Mud was on it. Granme was not one to add – as they do in the South – 'when you get to it.' What needed doing was to be done, and Mud instinctively knew if it wasn't he would be sent off the property. She had no use for layabouts and like all with royal blood was territorial.

He slept in the hearse but not in the rear like the deceased. He slipped into a back seat with the look of a Pullman compartment and pulled quilt over. Fall winter the tight space kept out drafts and slept him snug. I never saw him cold, red with warmth he came out of that compartment daybreak.

He dug a pit for wood and fried and ate bacon and eggs on a skillet he wiped clean with newspaper. He sowed a garden and raised red cabbage he watered naturally. He would pull an abnormality out of his pants and water like from hose. Looking out Granme not quite spit.

I wanted to like him but he was a sullen old Negro who didn't like men, born to serve women instead. As his reputation as a handyman grew slovenly whites brought him things to fix for a dollar. He shuffled for these white men, but you marked on his face the contempt for them when they walked off. He lived from a government check and a second pension check, both coming first of the month. One of few times he drove out of the gully was to bank those checks.

I never knew a father and here was someone who had campfire experience and could fix almost anything brought to him, but when I tried nudging up he shooed me away. He didn't like me from the second he saw me. I don't know if it was the white blood in me or that he was like old country dogs who won't abide younger.

I would hear from our white mailman this wasn't Ol' Mud's first turn in Louisville, that he had been around and wasn't the simple weatherbeaten old hand we took him for. First, he was the only infertile nigger who ever lived. Second, his complaints against the postal service would get him killed one day. He liked to start all-out tirades at the counter and had been jumped and beaten outside by postal workers.

End of summer Granme began bringing home a chicken to barbecue on Sunday, never inviting him to have a piece. He seethed around the hearse or over a gadjet he couldn't fix – all handymen have one that confounds them and they begin to treat like a pet. To get back at us he drove off and brought back a cut of round that overlapped the black skillet. Squat to fire, his bitterness come off, 'Western man eat off hoof,' he sniffed. 'Off hoof you cut loin tip round book buttquarter . . .' he saw me looking . . . '*balls* if you please – but a chicken nut'n but a goddam corpse.'

About to start third grade I hiked two miles to my old school, telling office ladies I feared my school. They said there was nothing they could do about it.

I was put in class with 18 girls 17 boys, all of whom hated each other. Miss Blessed brought a bible to cope. Benumbed of noise and fighting that went with it she seemed to go into godly reveries. I tried to be of service to her but was called a yellow-skin sissy and threatened. I answered nobody. Blindsided, cuffed on the ear, stomped on the instep, kicked in the pants I showed no hurt and for this reason was not beaten.

Miss Blessed stayed out days at a time and male teachers came in her place. It turned so wild that if one of those young men had put Miss Blessed's scissors on top of the desk and left the room locked behind him, by the time he got back one of us would have been on the floor dead. I was sure almost every boy and half the girls would see stone walls. Last to everything on the playground I found a corner of the fence. Chilly days I stole into the boiler room and sat in a nook biding time.

I got home two hours before Granme mama and after chores watched Ol' Mud puttering on something or other. I thought he would be impressed by a responsible eight-year-old, but when I started as to what adult work I might fit, he snuffed 'You ain' gon' be nut'n but a bus station habitué.' I think all boys seethe over an adult and think of ways to brain him; mine was to freeze a twenty-pound watermelon and drop it on his old woolly head from a flagpole.

Summer came and went with renewed hope of some intervention to keep me from going back to Carver. None come I signed up as an aide in the primary building. First grade teachers enjoyed my help and let me stay until recess. I did not go back to my room to line up for the yard – a risk in any bad class – but stalled until they were out. Returning with them I went back to the primary building after lunch to another first grade teacher, coming back to my room just before final bell.

It was work. Primary teachers, mostly middle-age glamour girls, did little as I went desk to desk spoonfeeding first graders. I also stopped by the handicapped class where attractive Miss Pierre appreciated my help. The idea came to transfer on the pre-text of my bent leg. I brought it up with her, saying I would like to be there for her all the time.

Teachers of these classes seemed to have privileges and she got me in. I was embarrassed to line up with the handicapped, seeing my former classmates looking, but I lived in fear and think this transfer saved me from furthur laming.

In this class I came across my cousin Clee who came in a first grader. He belonged to Granme's neice from a half brother winding up in Kentucky before going on the lam. I remember her coming to see us after we moved into the gully. She came in shiny black dress and red shoes, bringing a little boy, Clee. Granme wanted nothing to do with her. She had no husband, smelled of perfume and hair relaxant and had the red claws of a jaguar. Healthy as a horse she had no work at age 26. I thought Granme might put out tea and honey cake but she offered nothing, stonefaced as her niece described life across the field. To this day I wince at Granme's inhospitality. She could have put a little something out to make her feel welcome. It was her niece, daughter of a brother, but she sat mute told of hijinks and foolery at the projects. Granme thought if she showed more she would come back to leech.

She took Clee and walked off, cursing under her breath which I could read from her head and shoulders. I'd enjoyed playing with my little cousin, a wide-eyed chatterbox with a big round head, so to my surprise the new Clee was no longer a ball of fun but lean and sullen.

I did not reveal myself to him but gave him the most attention, teaching alphabet and numbers. He hated this instruction, why I know not. I asked Miss Pierre for his school folder where it was evaluated he couldn't tell a squirrel from a chipmunk.

It took no time to see it wasn't he couldn't learn; it was he would accept no teaching. As for thought I saw that when nobody looked he could put together a picture puzzle in minutes. He also had a lecherous eye for Miss Pierre and did not approve of a male teacher coming to visit. One morn she called me into the closet to help with materials. I came out to a leer I had come to know.

'Been tongue-kissin' with Miss Pierre?'

Tongue, the way he said it enraged me. I took him by the arm, 'See here, Clee! That talk won't do. That's low-class talk, not what we allow here.'

He sneered as though he hardly deemed me a figure of authority.

I saw more deviousness. A girl came and said Clee touched her in a secret place. Seeing him passing something to another girl I thought it was a vulgar sketch he liked to make of bespectacled male dogs with large genitals but it was writing she could not read.

You say you my girl. Why we ant had no six yet?

I wondered how anyone who couldn't tell a squirrel from a chipmunk wrote a note misusing only two words. It came to me, a ruse. He had faked his way into class to prey on little girls. I hurt I had a cousin of such character so I called him out, showing him the note.

'Nothing is slow with you, Clee. You hide here to get over on little girls. Any more monkeying I will tell boys on the yard you are touching their sisters and they will fix you. You want that?'

I had him scared but he sneered right back, 'What 'bout you, comin' in here all high and mighty, actin' a teacher – wutch you hidin' from?'

No way I might have answered would have done any good.

School let out Mama's pretty little face had bloated and hair had grown out on her chin. She retained water, became rounder and could no longer keep up with Granme. She still waved hello goodbye to one and all and all called her Dolly, but she began to loose sight. A tumor grew between her eyes that pressed against the optical nerve on each side. I woke on my cot before light. Granme stood over me with a candle. Mama was uncovered on the bed with her arms folded.

Granme took the little ring from her finger and cut off a curl of hair. They came from Louisville Medical School to pick her up. I lay on the bed with her, kissing her, rubbing her feet to bring her to. She was put in a van where I took my last look. An orderly sat down at the table, had Granme sign mama over and paid $75.

I knew no better then, but if I could find something of her now, a few bones to put in a piece of ground with a stone over it, I would pay every dollar I ever made – only a little corner of grass to come to and know she was there. I thought we'd grow old together and I would bring her little ones to play with and care for but it was not to be, and as I look back now I was cursed from early age.

Twelve and a half I started at Bethune Junior High, put in a class with boys who had abused me at Carver, only now some had grown slight mustaches and chin beards. Hallways were battlefields and these boys had become so long that with one bound they could punch across the width. Teeth hit the floor like marbles falling out of a sock. I gave thanks when I cleaned mine with baking soda all were there.

Boys had caught up with and passed girls in height and could now intimidate them. They made eyes in self-preservation, and word went round that some were doing mouth sex after school in old garages. Granme saw I carried no books and I told her it wasn't safe for a boy like me to carry books home. I didn't want a tooth knocked out or to lose an eye.

Falltime farmers came to schools with fruit they couldn't sell but got tax credit for. Bethune got a cardboard crate of pears hard as rocks. Hefting one in hand made you wonder if it could be bit. After lunch period one day I carried a note to the next building when a pear heaved from a third floor window knocked me cold. I awoke to dancing elves in circling light. I prided myself in the punishment I could take, but first, it was thrown from high gaining speed; second, it weighed a good five ounces; third, hard fruit does not ricochet like a rock but strikes 'falling not far from the tree' as is said. A meld of the three, I believe, knocked me cold. I did not have a 'glass jaw'; I proved that at Jefferson School many a time, slammed down, coming up for more.

I begged the school nurse not to let Granme know, but a note put to my hand was to be signed and returned. Granme did not read English. Told what happened she sat in silence.

Morn she called me to the table and said not to go to school but to take a bus downtown and bring back a few dollars each day, the way I brought quarters from the Pensions. It was as though a yoke of timber fell away. I was not being educated. Bethune taught me little if anything. But I was not yet thirteen and swung a leg, what work was there for me?

Granme put out a bowl of bean okra soup, a slice of rough bread and a dollar in change for me to strike out for myself. Walking Freeman Road I stopped the bus going downtown. Let off I found myself in Gin Alley. Louisville schoolboys talked of Gin Alley as a place where Fort Knox came to sin. At this hour trucks were double-parked delivering beverages, cases sent sliding down chutes because most gin joints were walkdowns. Rhythms of workers slinging merchandise befit those engaged in this business, ready they were to meet a soldier's hanker had he the price. The narrow buildings were so close together, sun was eclipsed but for a shaft here there.

Come to a sunny area of five and dimes, and arcades, I asked those in charge if they needed someone to sweep and run errands, only to be pointed out with 'Get along, boy.' Turning into an alleyway I saw a boy a year or two older brushing potatoes at a back door. This I could do, sitting on a soda box and working at a pace in the shade. He eyed me like he wanted to hand it over. I looked up at the sign on the bricks: *Louisville Steak Palace*. A worker eighteen or so came out, friendly like white boys who like to be around Negroes. He knew why I was standing there.

'How old are you?'

'Near fourteen,' I lied by a year, if that's a lie.

'You strong enough to handle a tray stack?'

'I'm strong and lift good.'

He took me into a cafeteria that served steaks on veneer trays instead of plates. I was to stack them up, bring them to the back and put them in a wash the size of a crate. Trays piping hot to be pulled out but gloves weren't around. The place was run by two Greek brothers and a cousin, finger-snappers for whom whatever you did was not fast enough. An oversize apron and paper hat were not easy to keep on straight as fast as I was expected to work. On the move the hop in my gait grew higher. Calling it a day the young white worker let me go, saying I was getting looks. He paid a dollar which I suspected came from his pocket.

Next day I got work at a counter from a man over sixty who did a nice little business because his breakfast and lunch plates were heaped with food and buttered bread. There was no waitress and the work was similar to that at the steakhouse, taking dishes back, wiping washing them clean. Day finished at two I sat at the counter waiting my pay. He called from the back. All morning he barely had the chance to look up. Now he stood rather erect at a small hand sink, his back to me. Sideways I peeked to see him lathering himself. I turned and fled out the front.

Rounding a corner I saw a sign for Savile Row. Even primary grade boys knew of Savile Row and boasted of fathers buying a $200 suit there. Of that time downtown businessmen wore suits, sportjacket and slacks too casual for a downtowner. Warehouse and factory men changed into suits after work. For a townsman thirty or more not to wear a suit

Monday through Friday would have people thinking he did mindless work. Louisvillians, Southerners in general, liked to be thought of as working and thinking at the same time; and if you wanted a good suit you went to Savile Row. Department stores sold stiff cloth.

Looking through windows I saw not the usual Louisville businessman. Darker complexioned, combed back instead of parted middle or aside, they sported showy watches and pointy shoes Southerners considered tacky.

Roundabout young Negroes carried suits that I took it were not theirs. Runners they were, delivering to downtown offices. Hardly shy to ask for work even with little idea of what I what I was getting into I went into Mel's. Two loud salesmen beheld me. I spoke not to them but to a finer man behind the counter.

'Do you need a go-getter, somebody to clean up?'

He saw I swung a leg. The salesmen, one 25 or so, the other twice over, complained I was too small, but the man I addressed was in charge and it seemed to me he winced at my packed up left shoe. A tilt in one shoulder did not tell me he too wore a little extra in a heel.

Checking his watch he asked the two if they were up for lamb? He wrote a note, handed me $5 from his wallet and pointed me downstreet to Greeks, to tell them the order was for Mel.

Unlike most meat when lamb gets cold half its flavor is lost. Unknowing then, one would have hardly thought so by the way I set to. A Greek packed the order in bags barely holding the sandwiches and coffee. A Greek will give you plenty to eat but a small bag to carry it in. I managed not to tip anything, bring it all back dry and set it on the counter, handing change to Mel. Peeking around the side I found a rag to wipe down the glass. The younger salesman said, 'What's he think he's doing?'

I became a runner there. I wasn't tall enough to deliver a suit hanging straight but Mel had a traveler in which a suit folded over. I would go to an office and tell the secretary I was from Mel's. The gentleman come out, I swung the suit up high. A good suit unfolds in a flow, it shows its breeding.

Taking compliments from the secretary he would tell her to give me 50 cents for a pack of cigarettes. I returned with the traveler in good stride, wanting Mel to see the sale was done. I understood that much when he put it in my hand. I had no other thought.

Twenty runners downtown I counted, alert Negroes who took instruction and saw it through. Some ran papers and checks from office to office. Busy real estate and law firms kept runners who moved smartly because they could be watched from upper floors. I didn't need to rush. A suit needed delivery in good time. It was hardly urgent.

As I got to know them I learned they spent their pay Saturday night. Sunday they had enough left for breakfast then eked out the week on tips. Byplay of the job to them to let off steam that way, I did not see why they could not as easily save their money.

I was making seven eight dollars a day, six days a week, which came to about half of what a grown Negroe took home. Blessed to be at Mel's, arrived I swept away debris out front. Proprietors asked I sweep their fronts while at it and I could have made a little change but I worked for Mel and would do nothing for his competitors.

After sweeping I sprayed and wiped glass. Next Mel handed me checks from yesterday to be hammered at the bank (cleared through) so Nate could start alterations. No suit was altered before the check was hammered, that done early because the difference from a good and bad check could be the light of day.

Checks deposited I was ready to deliver suits. Since they were to go out one at a time unless to the same customer it took about three hours bringing me to noontime. I would go for sandwiches, and then there was little to do. Now and then Mel sent me with $20 to the Louisville Hotel to place a wager, but mostly I stood around listening to him and the two salesmen. They stood as they talked because no good salesman will be caught sitting – to a customer it takes some vigor out of buying a suit.

A few weeks there, I learned the younger salesman, Jerry, was Mel's half brother. It took me by surprise. Mel was in his forties, not a tall man. His brother was six foot, with rough hair bumped skin. Moe, the other salesman, was sixty I guessed and somewhat desperate in speak as though he was hanging by a thread. Neither of the two gave me more than a glance.

I listened to the three of them talk politics, sports, gambling and fast characters present and past. To this day I think I remember everything said as I leaned on the counter chin in hand. Occasionally Mel left for an hour or two and Jerry and Moe went on about Las Vegas. They knew the casinos. Moe went every year. It was what he lived for. He had a former wife and grown son there.

One day as I stood listening Nate called me into his cove. 'You watch them talk. What good is it? Moe and Shmo – Las Vegas guys. Moe saves a thousand and walks into the casino like a big shot. His whole year is that day. Nobody knows he's nobody until the thousand is gone and he sits down to play keno with old ladies. Jerry, another talker, he fell in with hoodlums – burglary fencing. Not for Mel he would be sitting in jail. He lives with a girl, not Jewish, in River Towers. He would be there not for Mel? He would live behind Washington Street. Mel is a Las Vegas guy. He goes twice a year, loses wins, he doesn't change. He's Mel. You see a picture in back with Frank and Sammy? They look proud to be with him. *This* is a Las Vegas guy, not shits like

Moe and Jerry, and you stand listening with your mouth open. Tell me how old are you?'

'Thirteen.'

'What do you do with money you make, take it to your mother?'

'My Granme.'

'In that case it is not so bad you don't go to school. You don't run with nobodies hoodlums. You don't make bad friends.'

He pointed to *Reader's Digest* in stacks halfway up the wall. 'You can educate yourself; you don't need school. I was twelve years old my mother took me to a presser to put me on a machine ten hours a day to grow a hump and not reach five feet tall. She had no choice, seven children no husband, the oldest had to be a man. Still I knew I had to educate myself, that when I started going with a girl, not to embarrass myself to her family and friends, to be able to talk about what goes in the world. I never shamed my wife and her relatives with ignorant talk. The rabbi didn't talk down to me because he knew I was informed. I could sit with a table of rabbis and participate.'

He nodded to the stacks. 'Take one and read every afternoon. They won't run out. What you don't understand, ask. From each article commit the point to memory or it was for nothing. Each article will raise you so one day you can sit with educated people.'

Afternoon instead of listening to gab I sat with *Reader's Digest* then took home to read more. I educated myself about outstanding lives histories discoveries advancements. Truth in Nate's urging, if I kept up I would not be much diminished by not attending school. Finishing a story I discussed it with him. He seemed to remember them all and could add from more he knew. I didn't tire and he handed me a dime store book of crosswords to do every night, wordplay and reading going like bread and butter.

I also looked through the newspaper for something in particular. I had read of recent surgeries that improved vision and replaced roots for lost teeth, once lost causes. Glasses dentures could be thrown away. Not childish at thirteen I did not dream my left leg could be made to equal the right. I only wanted to push it forward as I walked on the street and not swing it out from behind.

I was learning of the world but in learning about people I watched Mel with customers, whether a city hall big shot or young downtowner who wanted to look sharp but could not afford a Mel Woorler suit. Mel would stand behind the counter in that way of his and give a young man a discount. Whoever you were you felt you were getting the top of the line for your money.

Mel favored no one but one sort he spoke of with contempt, millionaires called Abobs spread sparsely about the U.S. with a good few in the South. They were neither a society nor a secret society but a sense of one another, a knack to recognize brethren. Most of them inherited of wealth or big business, over long years do nothing to build it up yet do not run it down.

These Abobs live a life of self-deprivation. They drive Cadillacs for appearances sake but a Cadillac devoid of any accessory but a heater. There is no carpeting no radio. Cadillac Company knows of these skinflints and allows a small portion of their issue not to be appointed. To look inside one saw a Chevy taxi without the meter.

They reside in homes that befit their station, but with walls, velvet sets and carpets smelling of mold. Nothing new is done for fifty years. Feeding themselves they go the week on a supper of a can of Campbell chicken noodle, dipping cheap bread to fill their thin bellies. An apple banana is not brought into the house without occasion.

They are wiry giving a look of being tall and usually marry of their physical description, not wanting an eater to feed. In marriage leanness is sacrosanct, saving in food until with age their hip bones grow out of their rumps and spines curve up high like a biblical Hebrew's staff. There is hatred of Jews in every fibre of their being. Secretly intolerant of anyone unlike them, their abstemious nature holds it in, but about Jews it seeps out.

Two came in one Saturday, one straighter than the other who had already formed the Hebrew staff. They were Pillsburgs who with two other brothers owned sawmills in Kentucky and Southern Indiana, a company going so far back the outlaw Frank James had been one of their salesmen. Sniffing round, the one in a straw boater fingered a price ticket to his brother who beheld Mel.

'Is it true Jesus was a Hebrew blood?'

'That's what they say?'

He checked the tag again. 'I bet when one weren't lookin' he could skin a cat with the best of 'em.'

'Why?' asked Mel. 'You been skinned by a Jew?'

'Who ain't – most folks tell ya'.'

'What else you heard?'

'Well, I hear time to time they'll take a younger, preferably male, bleed him for that special bread *motzo*. That's no hearsay, that got history. I won't eat that bread.'

'You believe that?'

'I don't see why not?'

'Let me tell you something about Jews,' said Mel. 'No Jew ever lived who could stand the sight of blood. It's in their souls. Kosher butchers salt out so much blood no taste is left. Jews step back from blood. If they didn't every other Jew would be a surgeon. A Jew would bleed a *child?* No people love children like Jews. My mother in Chicago fed half the tenement; the screen door was always open the pot never empty.'

'That so?' he laughed like it was beyond belief.

40

'Another thing – you don't want to be taken by a Jew don't pray to one. A hippie on a donkey trots around spreading the word of God, a thousand years later savages forge steel, hold up a cross and go slice the throats of any man woman and child who won't bend to it. When Jews lived by the Five Books of Moses and walked in great halls those savages you come from were shitting in caves and breeding with their daughters.'

'That so?' It was obvious he would reply no other way.

'Keep believing no Jew ever spent a dime, you know, your brother knows, if shit didn't stink you'd both eat it twice a day. A *Jew* would kill a child for his *blood* . . . don't look at my tickets. I don't want you wearing my suits.'

I watched them leave, narrow shoulders high in back. I went to Nate.

'Did you hear that?'

'He opened a big mouth for satisfaction; he'll pay for it. You always pay for opening a big mouth. It's not for free.'

There was another sort who came in, go-betweens who brought buyers. Agile characters with no overhead, they slipped a fifth of the mark-up into their pockets like it was nobody's business. Dealing in autos wristwatches furs suits, some brought business to face surgeons. They knew anybody in town with money falling out of his pockets but would admit that wasn't doing business. Doing business, they liked to say, was bringing someone with no money to someone with nothing to sell and dealing from pure air – *that* to them was business! Twenty-percenters brought buyers to Mel and I watched, asking myself where would I ever get the money to run a line of goods? Only learning this go-between would I become more than a runner or clerk.

Nate told me the *Reader's Digest* stacks wouldn't run out but they did. I went to the library and took books on historical individuals, even taking time to enjoy poetic tales of freebooters on high seas and Tarzan in the jungle. I'd been at

Mel's four years and had developed a style of dress that suited my work: white shortsleeve shirt blue gray pants and matching cravat. Never was I unbuttoned without necktie, overdressed for what I did. In fall winter I went about in a tan canvas duster with epaulets and blue lapels. It looked neither civilian nor military but of service industry, hotel provision I took it. A uniform all in all but what in my short years had not been functional and makeshift?

The store radio gave public service announcement for an equivalency certificate accepted in lieu of high school diploma. Calling the number I was told to go to the Federal offices downtown above the post station. On the second floor I took a booklet and was told the next test was on the second Saturday of July. I was to bring a social security card and there would be no charge.

I looked through the booklet on the bus home. The reading part straightforward I easily answered sample questions. Back at the gully I did number calculations. Terms unacquainted with: quotients products ratios, I took meaning by association. Monday I went to the Social Security office and was issued a card and number.

I went to Mel, asking off on the twelfth to take the test. It mattered not little. I delivered three four suits Saturday.

Five applicants came. Reading comprehension I went through in forty minutes. Mathematics next I came upon unknown-number exercises. Untrained in equations I reasoned out ratios. Science and Social Studies were no more than reading comprehension in their content. I wrote a short essay and handed in pencil and booklet, sure I would get my certificate.

Six weeks on I received a letter in government cover asking me to come see Mr. Kell at the GED office. I was there on opening. Looking at the letter he opened my folder.

'Daupin Capet, you made 100 reading, that got it all, 95 math. Considering your age the government has schooling available. You are almost 17 and have a sixth-grade education.'

'Yes.'

'Why did you stop?'

'Granme told me to go bring money home. I was getting little out of school.'

'Let me guess – you privately read everything you got your hands on including the Heinz catsup bottle?'

'I read every day and don't take it lightly. I try to get the point else I don't believe I truly read.'

'We get unschooled readers but math trips them up. Equations unknowns usually puzzle when one hasn't taken algebra and geometry and I would guess you didn't study those subjects.'

'No, though I run numbers in my head and play with them in riddles.'

I sensed it was to Mr. Kell's official credit to come across my type.

'If you're interested in starting college the government will cover tuition and books required.'

'I am grateful the government would do this but I must bring home money for now.'

'What work do you do?'

'I deliver suits but I would like to go on to higher education.'

'Call me when, we'll get you started. You are a fellow the government has in mind for these benefits.'

The certificate came and I showed it to Granme telling her it was almost a high school diploma. I framed it, putting it up over my cot.

Granme lost her place at the Robinson's. Finished with a long federal project the husband was called back to D.C. I took it she would be referred to a similar job because I read to her cards from the Robinsons' guests thanking Granme for looking after their children, but I think she no longer had the will to leave the gully. Something had gone out of her. Her China doll was gone; the Robinson children were along in school and I think she had no more spirit to go to another family. She made up a sign for alterations, attached it to a post hammered down at the curve of our road. Then on she would sew. I thought little of it but coming home knowing Granme was inside and not at the Robinson's, I got a feeling the first part of my life had come to an end.

In my fifth year with Mel downtown the lifestyle of mod hippies penetrated the South. Suit and necktie were now only for square birds. Savile Row weakened, smaller stores converting to clothes with collars and lapels the size of a clown's. It seemed more suit business would go to Mel but turned out not. Weekends Mel transported suits to an empty store in a suburban area, selling on Saturday and Sunday, Sunday a day he never worked before.

I had grown to five two, a lean 120 pounds from blocks I walked, brisk air I breathed, natural foods I was given to eat all my life. Babyfaced and curly as a Spaniel I thought I would grow taller, but five two I stayed, changed of voice. I'd been bringing money to Granme since twelve and a half, educating myself on *Reader's Digest*, crossword puzzles and library books, thinking at times on the bus that if I had not been kicked by a macoute and mangled by a fake doctor I would be a young man to be reckoned with. I had little violent zeal but that macoute's crazed eyes came to mind. Some nights I could not sleep of them.

Most suit runners went to other work. Waldo ferried documents by bike over the river, so trustworthy he was paid per delivery and took a paycheck. He told me he was buying land on both sides of a creek in Arkansas and within the twelvemonth with God's help he would go live off the land, get himself a woman and walk his property with a dog – and who would know he had run papers and answered to 'boy'?

I told him I would learn a trade and he suggested I cut hair Saturday Sunday at a shop called De Carlo's. A runner he knew learned there then went to Alaska to team up with his father, making $250 a week off laborers.

I flinched at the thought of barbers making that. He told me De Carlo's was by the river in an area called the Flats. I went Friday after work. It was on grooved road, with a wide porch in front, a high pole in back like telegraph offices I'd seen in old tintypes of Louisville. I climbed steep wood staircase. Two Negroes were cutting hair. A short one with thick glasses told me to call him Lemon and that the job was to keep the place swept and toilet fresh. Otherwhile I would stand at his side learning to cut. De Carlo was out of town and when he came back he would decide to keep me or not. Else a funky waft it seemed all right there but for a shoeshine stand at the wall. I knew it would cause trouble the second I saw it.

Come to work Saturday I straightened out the back, cleaned privy, then took opposite of Lemon. He would snip one side of a customer and pass me scissors and comb to snip the other, pleased at how I imitated. Noon a sturdy Negro got up on the stand.

'Daupin, shine him up,' Lemon chortled his back turned. 'Box is open. Get you a few bits on those gators.'

I came with a whisper. 'I don't want to shine shoes. I'll do other things, I don't want to shine shoes.'

I thought he might send me home but he said 'Youngblood says he don't shine shoes.'

The Negro rose and left. Afterward I swept the floor around Lemon who sat cleaning his glasses.

'Why you don't shine shoes, youngblood? Is it you light, the man dark?'

'I am not racist. I come from Haiti and my blood flows back to Louis XVI, last King of France. Shining another man's shoes isn't something I should do.'

A policeman Turnbow came every day in or out of uniform, the largest negro I'd seen, six three, 240 pounds with a bad reputation in Louisville. He married Mrs. Johnson, a teacher at Carver I had helped, a handsome woman whose first husband Dr. Johnson died before his time. Two years on she married Turnbow, indication of what steady income could get a black man – a college-educated woman marrying a near illiterate – a dog with ears as he was known in the Flats. I heard her say in the teachers lounge that on their wedding night he stood up in the tub flapping his thighs together and she asked herself how anybody that big could have something that small?

He was a jailer in the U.S. Army in Germany. Returned stateside he found work as a sweep. For all his jail work he was claustrophobic and one night locked himself in the cellar only to be found morn with his lungs screamed out. He eventually got a uniform and shot a man in the foot, killing him and getting a reputation. Not long after he was nearly cashiered.

Early Seventies, soldiers returned from Viet Nam no longer able to live a civil life and teamed up as armed robbers working the Kentucky Indiana line, back and forth across the river. Known as deadly shooters, two with M1s were trapped at the 880 Motel. Turnbow was in the vicinity. Word was he was at the motel when shooting started, ran out on the street yelling *Lookout!* to no one in particular and crawled under a truck so that only the bottom of his boots showed. It was so appalling he was brought before a board to answer to statements from citizens. Negro White relations in Louisville were flammable and City Hall deemed the charges too touchy and put them down. A month later Turnbow redeemed himself. A camera crew from Channel 7 News began tailing police cars to film arrests for a crime segment *Street Stop!* They came on the pitiful sight of Turnbow cornering a drug addicted girl pleading 'Please don't hurt me, my mother is a doctor!' Seen from behind in leather jacket Turbow said 'Yo' mama, a doctor? You look like you come from a prostitute.' Next day white Louisville was abuzz over this huge black policeman who spoke his mind regardless of color. He was interviewed on TV news, invited to businesses for free goods and to downtown functions where he spoke in banalities, without original thought: about women – *get'm to smile they go that extra mile*; a political outcast – *bastard at a family reunion;* hunger for graft – *like a bulldog after the meat wagon*. He ogled both food and women, and invitations stopped.

It was said there was no decency in him, he just walked a side of the fence. His reply to any crime no matter how cruel was *'funky as a brass monkey!'* He bore it no ill will, meaning no more to him than *Howdy do?* To this day as I describe him I can't comprehend how this fat villain was able to steal my wife and make me flee Louisville.

Saturday came a taxi with De Carlo. Come up the staircase in fur collar he flipped a box on the counter, twirling his fingers as though it was for everyone. It was a near weightless flat of candy chocolate you see in dime store bins after spring clean-up. Easing down in a barber chair he let the collar embrace him.

'How's your mama, De Carlo?'

'I think I seen her for the last time, Lemon.' It was the only time I would hear him call Lemon by name.

'Tis pity, De Carlo. Is her strength gone back?'

'She saved some, get'n help to the table every mornin' to say, "De Carlo, you so handsome, why you not married like your brothers?"'

He lit a cigarette and sucked something out between his teeth. 'Yeh, De Carlo follow his brothers and be sold into slavery like Joseph. Your time yours no more your money yours no more your way of life no more. Give it all to a woman, go toil with your back and sides and come home nights to the same pussy served cold. That livin' or animal husbandry?'

Lemon was gleeful. 'De Carlo, you tell the public what it's all about.'

De Carlo was just warming up. 'I got a brother like a Missouri mule, don't turn his head, don't know what's goin' on roun' him, don't want to. Just keep ploddin', know where he got to go and get there.'

Lemon needed to stomp a foot. 'De Carlo, you too much.'

'Teachers said, "De Carlo, you don't snap to like other boys." I answer "De Carlo don't react, De Carlo think." Talk to the brothers doin' twenty-five to life downstate, ask what they did – react or think?'

Turnbow came in a light blue cardigan and soft loafers, sitting down as easy as Ozzie Nelson. Here I would see a test of personalities, looking for which one would give way. Turnbow reached to tap De Carlo's hand put up just enough to tap back. My notion was that from De Carlo Turnbow got a lazy man's hangout, and De Carlo's as a business got an aura of police patronage. Else I sensed neither would lift a finger to help the other and they may have disliked one another.

'How's Atlanta?' asked Turnbow.

'Livin' large. Whites turned service industry – white and blue collar. My cousin got a job with Andrew Young and go to luncheons to answer white peoples' questions. Took me with him to Four Winds. I remember when they didn't let a boy work there less he was high yella or red. Jeter so black he disappear after dark, and here we sittin' with fancy white women.'

Turnbow came in on his favorite subject – white peoples' dinners. 'What they serve, De Carlo?'

'Chicken Cordon Bleu; first they bring soggy lettuce with bread rind, got nerve to call it Caesar Salad.'

'Caesar Salad!' chortled Lemon. 'That's what white people eat when they can't shit.'

De Carlo tapped his polished nails. 'I got ready to grab one of those white shavetails to bring me some greens and fatback. Did they think Caesar Salad was gonna hold a Southern black man?'

Lemon added 'Don't think he wouldn't. Louisville gonna turn same way and we gonna be here to see it.'

'They takin' applications for Sunday Briars luncheons,' said George the other barber. 'They stand you back with linen over your arm. White men go to the head let a fart just to show you who you is. Don't you blink neither! One day it's gonna be us lettin' farts at them.'

'Amen! Amen! Amen!' danced Lemon.

De Carlo didn't join in. 'Black thing get'n out of hand. Prostitutes up and down Martin Luther King Boulevard, datin' in cars, leavin' their shit over the road – hurt my feelings.'

Lemon summoned Turnbow. 'They need you to come clean house.'

'Amen! Amen!' cheered George.

Saying nothing to that De Carlo looked down at his slippers. 'I didn't miss all this red Louisville dust. Go all day not get no dust on your shoes.'

Lemon motioned across. 'De Carlo, our new man Daupin zigzaggin' roun' here like all get-out. He wipe windows with vinegar.'

A half drop eye rose from his slippers. 'I see you ain't at nuthin' now. Come over here, shine me up.'

'Oh, that's one thing,' excused Lemon, 'he don't shine a man's shoes 'cause he got royal blood.'

De Carlo swung round. 'What kind royal blood you got?'

'My blood goes back to Louis XVI and Marie Antoinette.'

'That make you too good to shine shoes? A man come here to get clean, you got the heart to let him walk out in funky shoes?'

Lemon and George added grunts. De Carlo turned away but I knew he had it in for me now.

Come Saturdays Sundays I was amazed at his airs. Picking something up or putting it down he gave his fingers a twirl. Sometimes he talked to customers sometimes not but never cut a man's hair straight through. Twice at least he stepped away for no other reason than to look through a drawer or stack of mail, letting him sit. Why these men didn't object I don't know?

He was a beauty consultant and women came for appraisals. Some were delusional and when they came up the porch De Carlo ran out to shoo them away. 'Naw! Naw! You ain't ready for Miss Black Louisville, go to County Fair.'

His standards met he assayed thigh and buttock not with tape measure but clipboard, pressing here there, telling her where to trim. For this advice he took $5.

He was the gamiest eater I ever saw and Negroes can be gamey eaters. He had poor circulation in a leg and did not sit between cuts, staying on his feet. He'd open a tin of mustard sardines on the counter and pick at them. Not sardines he opened a tuna can hardly more than catfood and picked at that. White tuna white chicken tasted like wood pulp to him and he dismissed them. Saturdays an elderly lady brought him a plate of mustard greens and turkey butts that stank up the shop and left me queasy. Trapped once between him and the plate, his bluish check brushed mine. My nostrils stiffened taking hold of his breath. *God Almighty!* My toes wanted to tear the soles out of my shoes. I extricated myself the instant I was but overcome.

Learning different cuts of black men's heads can make you money in the army a work gang or any place black men congregate because black men like to look sharp no matter what the circumstances, even locked up.

Little to invest in: buzzer scissors brushes combs talcum frock, I could go earn in the community – side money it is called – and if not for side money how could Granme mama I have survived? How could we have come to this good land America?

Lemon would start a head on one side, step around and let me at the other. I began to see how to make a narrow head look thicker a thick head narrower, perceptions a barber should have. My weakness was with the buzzer on a cut called the roll. I needed leverage but was embarrassed to stand on a soda box as Lemon suggested. I didn't have the vantage to run a buzzer straight over a skull without catching it on loose skin a knot or blemish, what Negroes have more than a fair share of.

Mel's business slowed to half. He was not there one Monday, gone to Miami to stake out a new store Nate said.

I stood like one bereft. 'How long do you think it will be?'

'A suit store you paint walls make a sign bring in carpet and stock. It is not complicated. He is not making money.'

'What are you going to do?'

'My wife and I are comfortable in our flat – but sit and look at each other? We'll go to Miami . . . why not? I don't know how much longer my eyes will work but when they stop I'll be in the sun with Jews, not here in Louisville, Kentucky. Come.'

'I can't leave Granme.'

'Take her.'

'I don't think I could talk her into going.'

'There is a future in Miami for a young man. Miami will be a finance depot. Cubans are lifting their heads. Money from Central and South America moves there. It is ready to grow rich. I'm an old man and feel excitement.'

'I have been with Granme every day of my life. I would not leave now.'

Mel did not come back that week. Only a suit or two to be delivered each day, I was no longer given checks to deposit and Jerry did not send me for sandwiches. Moe hitching up his pants went himself.

I had no more to do there Jerry was letting me know. I tried to make a little work for myself but to no matter. He didn't call me over to pay me as Mel used to from the register. I determined to go to De Carlo's seven days a week, finish training and find a good place to use it.

I told Granme I had no more work on Savile Row and wanted to hurry my way at De Carlo's. She nodded to this more readily than I thought she would. Rid of any last notions of being a suit runner, I had always entertained that Mel would bring me along and begin me as a salesman but apparently he had nothing in mind that way.

Bringing no money back to the gully, the days felt hollow. Granme had begun to fade at the machine doing what I thought was impossible of her – making mistakes. I came in on a woman giving it to her for ruining a dress, accusing her of stupidity. I had never seen anyone so enraged. Granme took out her purse and paid her $8.

It was not long before she put away the machine, saying her eyes weren't good enough. She sat for hours lamenting to herself. She missed the little girl who had tagged along behind her. I always knew I came second to her China girl. She called me mama's name and kept on even after I corrected her. I saw her slipping into her own world. She had enough purpose to her morning duties but once she sat down she did not want to get up. I boiled spaghetti with shank bones like she used to but she said she couldn't eat.

Under spare light she sat tapping her lips, and I asked myself if this was all her life had amounted to – a matter of survival, of never enjoying herself, of affording little to sweeten the way, of sending her little girl to be cut into parts instead of laying her in good ground and a stone over her with her name and years? Bethought of this I was one eve, she called me to her, taking my hand.

'Do not be an inferior as I was. Be true to your name. Make a fight of it. Something will come your way. It will so.'

I did not remember waking before Granme. Always she stood over me. So waking to sunlight something was not right. Thinking she was in privy I saw her on her side against the wall. I turned her up, patting her cheeks. She gave a blink and mumbled she would be all right.

I tried to give her water but she turned her head. Cooling her face and hands with a dishrag, I took coins, ran to the market on Freeman Road and called Emergency.

I found her back on her side. Turning her up from behind I lifted under her arms and rocked her up and down. Medics came but couldn't get a word out of her. I asked what happened. One whispered 'heart.'

Hurrying down Freeman Road I caught a bus to the hospital and was shown to Emergency. Granme had expired. Drawn off by curtain her eyes were up to the light, the teeth she had cared for all her life apart in a wry smile.

I had not cried for mama though I loved her more but cried over Granme like a lost child. She was in a wrap, her things on a chair. I got out her canvas utility belt from under her nightdress. The knots were gone. Always she had four five attached. I took the belt to the nurse telling her Granme attached valuables to it. She called an orderly who said there had been nothing on the belt.

Pulling up a chair I took Granme's hand. The nurse asked where I wanted her sent. Seeing I had no idea she suggested letting the county hold her. Granme was moved out into a walkway to a side entrance. I stood by until the morgue attendant arrived.

Returned to the gully I lifted Granme's mattress and looked through the two valises. An ambulance man or someone at the hospital had removed the knots. There would have been at least the one with mama's lock of hair and ring. I wanted to go back and complain but who would listen? Else I had no idea what she had knotted up. She let me know little if anything.

I sat over tea and a little marmalade with no money to bury her, not even an idea of how much to put her in good ground. Going to the market I called Reverend Brown.

'Our days are numbered,' he breathed. 'Your Granma Olivia was a blessing, a gift from God. Raise your eyes, Daupin. "Oh, Master, let Olivia walk with thee, and help Daupin bear her passing."'

'Reverend Brown, she is in the morgue. I have no money to see to her.'

'She has jewelry, rings? Women have these things even if they don't wear them. Do you own the trailer the land?'

'We rented.'

'We can put her to rest for $800. Come near, I can see it done plain and respectable like she was. Sit think, something will come to you.'

I took a bus downtown finding County Morgue next to the jail, told a body is kept for at least five days before it is put in a common grave along with who else is abandoned over this time. Outside came a thought as Reverend Brown said it would. Granme had a dime store print on the wall of handsome couples at a square dance, gals in hoop skirts and frilly blouses, beaus in jeans rolled up over boots. She had said to look in back if anything happened to her. I expected only to find a document linking me to France's throne.

Returned, I put the frame on the table. Lifting metal tabs with my thumb I removed cardboard in back, finding title to the gully. I had always suspected that we took in more money than the frugal amount we lived on. Granme had no bankbook

54

I ever saw. End of the month she bought a check, filled it out at the table and put it in the mail next day. I had not seen her do this of late.

At Louisville Bank as it opened I was shown upstairs. The upper half was not a full floor but a railed track officers could look over. A tall young man Mr. Rooda sat me down and I explained my situation. He looked up the property and said it was appraised at two thousand. I could get more he said but it would take time. He recommended I take out a loan similar to a car lien. The bank would lend me $1500 which I would repay $60 a month for three years. There was a hitch: title in Granme's name.

He handed me pad and pen. 'Take down: I, Olivia Overuse, of sound mind, leave to my grandson, your name, all personal and real property known and unknown with no exception or exclusion.'

I repeated it to him.

'Get it typed. I'll give you a copy of your grandmother's signature. Date it back eight nine months, sign in her hand best you can. Use your weak hand. The difference can be explained in the tremors old people get. Come noon I'll have the forms.'

I went to the library and waited for a typewriter. In several trys I pecked out what I had written. On wasted pages I practiced Granme's signature with my left hand. Returned to the bank I was given forms to sign. Mr. Rooda suggested an account and made up a bankbook. Thanking him I went downstairs to a window and drew out $1000.

My work not whole until I saw Granme into good ground, I could not leave it to others. From newspaper accounts of coroners expediting unclaimed bodies and blackhearted undertakers' abuses of the deceased I knew to trust in neither.

I called Reverend Brown. He told me to go to Fleeman Bros. Mortuary on Morgan Road and get papers signed.

Taking a bus there I sat down with one of the brothers. His jowels twitching in greed I told him Reverend Brown sent me for the $800 funeral. He knew I didn't have much but he was going to get all he could.

'Plots are up.' He worked out an expense sheet. 'It'll come to $875 – a pine box. That what you want for granma?'

'She was plain. She wouldn't have wanted better.'

'I need cash up front.'

'I have money.'

'You want padding in the box, twenty bucks or so. She gonna be a long time gone.'

He added $30 to the contract making it $905. He turned the sheet to me. I did not take the pen.

'First I want her brought from the morgue before she is put in a common grave.'

'We'll have her tomorrow.' He insisted I sign.

'First she must be here.'

He snorted this was irregular.

'Bringing her first thing we need $100 up front.'

I paid, saying I would be early at the morgue.

'Leave it to us,' he said, come from the mouth of a charlatan lets you know there is cause to doubt.

Early out front at the morgue three hours passed and no Fleeman Bros. truck. I called Calvin Fleeman on the phone inside.

'Mr. Fleeman, where is your vehicle?'

'On early runs.'

'How long will you say?'

'An hour, no more.'

It went by, then another. I called again, told his boy was bending my way. I waited two more hours.

'Mr. Fleeman, he is not here.'

'Daupin, you know the morgue isn't so fast to dump a body. We've picked up there for quite some time.'

56

'I won't depend on that. He is not here by four I will walk downtown to find another place to do this. I do not see what is so hard about picking up my Granme.'

A van came. One look at the driver I would not have trusted him to walk a dog around the block. Granme was wheeled out. I asked to see her. The morgue attendant opened a canvas bag on a half frozen face and I touched her wizened cheek.

Arrived with Granme I paid Calvin Fleeman in full and took a copy of contract. My last request was the casket be open on delivery to good ground. I had read too much about morticians not to be sure to the last.

I took a bus to Unity finding Reverend Brown still there, his hours usually short. He saw I was peaked and said we would do it Friday and he would bring the sisterhood. He asked if I would put out a platter for $25.

On hillock of rough ground I took my last look at Granme before she was lowered. My eyes fluttering like a child's Reverend Brown called me in front of ten women and four men to bless me for seeing to her. At the repast I sat alone. The sisterhood chattered, already forgotten of Granme, and I wondered once I was gone to good ground who would be left to remember there was once a Granme and little China girl who tagged along behind her? It was as though it was all for nothing. Returned to the gully I took Granme's clothes to the bin on the Carver School lot.

Maytime road gangs came to Louisville to blacktop road. Most Louisville Negroes looked a third white. Kentucky Negroes I long heard tell were never dark field hands. They worked in stable or in house. For backstraining work like tarring road rough Negroes came from deeper south. Unlike many migrant laborers they did not drink and watched their money. They came to De Carlo's Sundays for the dollar roll, paying mostly with rolled up pennies. The dollar roll required curving the buzzer around and over the skull, low over one ear, across the flank, straight over the top, across the other flank and over the ear. Then it took a smaller buzzer to clean up hedgerows – plain enough but they were tall leaving me no vantage over their heads. I could have brought out the soda box to stand on but convinced myself I could traverse the top by feel. I'd done much by feel alone.

A rainy Sunday they came all at once. De Carlo said to work a chair. A nemesis is no nemesis without timing. He knows best when to put you in distress. He will wait patiently until the moment. Eyeing the embittered Negro in the chair, the buzzer trembled in my hand. Lemon suggested the soda box, but I stepped to and ran the buzzer around his ear and high across the flank. From nape of neck up over his skull, thinking I was clear, the teeth caught. *Uuuh!* Up came two murderous eyes and a clenched fist. Blood on his fingertips he eased back into the chair. I finished the other side, cleaned up hedgerows, powdered him. He paid with penny rolls.

Four waiting, two more came out of the rain, road work called off. At grumbling I was palmed off on them I imagined what they thought of my light skin and curly hair, but royal blood seeks to win the day. If I got through them, learning the dollar roll under fire, I would fear no customer again.

Traversing the next two heads, just as I thought I had the feel of it I was but stomped to death. Yanked off my feet, feeling nothing under me, I was swung out the door and kneed down the stairs. Jerked over the curb by my frock and run headfirst into the barber pole, I was pulled off by one leg, kicked in the buttocks and stomped end to end. Rolled up in a ball, profanites coming down with each thud of his foot, I turned an eye up at the front window and saw DeCarlo lighting himself a smoke.

I flagged down a bus in the rain. Riders asked if I'd been mugged. To pounding skull and stiff jaw I gave little concern because my ribs were cracked. Bending around felt like a blade slicing through me. I wobbled to the trailer, got out of wet clothes and lay down flat working my jaw. Needing to urinate I propped myself up and went to privy. Easing myself back to bed my buttocks collapsed with a bolt of pain that shot up through my temporal bones. An elbow balanced underneath me I turned over flat. Wind getting through the thin door a sneeze might have finished me. My rib cage would have splintered and punctured an organ. I could not have survived it.

Awake before light with a lump in my jaw I got a leg over the side, pushing up from hip and elbow. Lowering myself on privy my sphincter without support from my ribs could not constrict.

I ate nothing three days, rising from bed as though pulling myself out of ice water with shards like broken glass. Several times I held off a sneeze that would have not only splintered my ribs but cracked my jaw. I might have survived one, not both.

Bethought I lay – a man in health fancies easy money; in convalescence he is undeluded. I had noticed just about every customer at De Carlo's losing hair asked if it could be stopped. De Carlo palmed off vitamins and oils but admitted no one ever said they worked.

One of Granme's sidelines in the mulatto compound was treating hair loss. All else done she took a bucket out the gate and went up a path to the old soldiers home where she ladeled urine from a trough. Mixing it with vinegar, letting it stand overnight, she rubbed it into heads with over-colored over-relaxed hair. Using her fingers, holding that urine had antiseptic qualities, she scrubbed a head again and again, covering it with a plastic cap to build up pressure. Sounds like *Zounds!* came from these women, fumes penetrating skulls, seeping into follicles, waking them like two nostrils by an ammonia capsule snapped to. A week or two, baby hair grew.

Wiley mulatto women envious of Granme's moneymaking cornered me to ask what the potion was made of, taking away naught. Taught early only a fool will tell a family secret to please a stranger I was mute to them.

I would not apply it by hand like Granme but bottle and label it, selling door to door until word-of-mouth begot distribution from warehouse to stores and barbers.

I knew ribs healed on their own, when they felt like it. Mindful of a strict feeling of not moving my bowels, I went down Freeman Road to the market and brought back a container of sour cream and box of prunes. Fixing myself a plate I minced with my front teeth, I remained stopped and took a bus to Daisy Drugs downtown, pleading six days without a movement.

Suggested an enema I was reluctant, recalling an apperatus in Mrs. Sperlock's privy, rubber bag and hose that looked it could service a racehorse. Pointed to small containers holding rubbery bottles I took one back to the trailer, letting down my pants, lifting my testicles and inserting bottle point. Squeezing tight I rushed to privy. *Oooooooh! Aaaaaah!* Chills running up and down my spine I let a length shaped like a railroad spike, followed by sprays of hardened bits and a shrill like of foundry horn that breezed so I begged it would not stop. Lathering both hands I wobbled to bed.

From good ground sowed came a second letter from Mr. Kell at the GED office, asking me to stop by. I went downtown to the Federal Building. On second floor to the right, I sat in a draft through perpendicular windows. Fine breeze and someone wanting to see me along left me with fond memory of the old building. I was called.

'Here we are,' Mr. Kell greeted me. 'If you're ready to start college we can get you on as a teacher's assistant with Louisville School District. You'll work morning, be free to take classes afternoon and evening. Stick to it you'll be paid $250 a month, government picking up the cost.'

He handed me a packet.

'There you have vouchers for tuition and books. Lab costs and such, come by, we'll try to cover that.'

I thanked him.

'A boy like you who educated himself, we need to get you going.'

He handed me a booklet on college student etiquette I looked through in the lobby. Walking over to the University of Louisville Downtown Extension I registered with Admissions, then sat with a counselor who looked through the freshman schedule and suggested I take World Civilization and Psychology available eves. Classes would start fall.

Louisville School District four blocks away I was processed as a teacher's assistant, told I could begin next day, assigned to Clemmens Elementary, the largest in the district.

Showing up morn on Sixth and Griffith I was sent to the primary building to Mrs. Lott who gave me no instruction, saying only 'Go help them!' She was a ten-year primary teacher and knew what she could get away with. She and others like her in the building showed up not a minute early nor stayed five minutes over. In class they did little more than take attendance.

A class of second-graders who did not complete the required work during the school year, they had workbooks for reading spelling arithmetic and when they brought them to Mrs. Lott she pointed them right to me, even when she saw my hands were full. Surrounding me they cawed like chicks in a nest.

Most of them scribbled what they wanted to in answer spaces, hardly more legible than chicken scratch in dirt. Desk to desk I explained reading and number exercises, bent over pained ribs until I saw a right answer plainly written. Pawing me left right it was hard for them to understand that the one I was with needed my help as they did. I let them paw. It did not annoy me. The class began to learn under my care, a natural urge to service. Even a small one knows if he is learning or wasting time, and will adjust his efforts. I thought Mrs. Lott might take pride in their improvement, even though she had nothing to do with it, but it made no difference to her if there was learning or not. She sat with good posture looking through magazines, her checkbook or a report from the Teacher's Union. I wondered if it was just summertime but would see she and others like her were not much different during the school year, this sloth perpetual. They were there only to claim a paycheck.

Classes over at 11:15 I took the class to cafeteria, watching over them until noon bell, my pay $12 for about three hours of instruction. Come August I began to wonder if I, who had not spent a day in high school, would make a college student.

Late in the month I went to College Bookstore and picked up text and syllabus for both classes. The World Civilization book was not easy to follow – was a World Civilization book ever written in a non-pompous way? Leafing through pages on the bus I stopped at a face resembling mine in long forehead oval eyes soft chin: Marie Antoinette, my granme many times back. Back forth from her to text, I read about the French Revolution, my forbears and the villains and rabble who brought them down.

Eve over the same pages, I came to see the course as not so much historical facts as dynamics of the times and to read with that in mind.

Summer school finished three weeks before the new school year. Me one of two aides to accept yard assignment for those weeks it was no more than keeping some order among gradeschoolers who came to play. Midday to eve I read the texts down to fine print.

I started classes on a Monday. My instructors, older white men, assigned reading portions, attaching modern social comment to them. I would see that college teachers attach social and political notions to the subject at hand. They were plainspoken and I had no trouble following. All but one of my classmates were men, some retired army personnel some managers of downtown stores wanting to better themselves. The female, a blond nurse, wished to go into another field.

At Clemmens Elementary I was assigned to the primary building again but to different rooms. Mrs. Lott was so unfazed by my tutoring she didn't ask to get me back. Instead she was given a college boy who spoke like a white teenager. He had counseled at a summer camp, telling stories to Mrs. Lott and others in the lounge of quick couplings with mothers who came for weekend visits. To believe or not I didn't know. He was confident but I would see in life that the best liars, of course, are the ones you would bet tell truth.

Primary teachers were all glamour girls like Mrs. Lott. Upon arrival they flaunted new outfits and shoes. Ranging in age a school day to them was no more than an outing with bakery treats instead of sensible sandwiches. They gossiped about family, neighbors and most of all men, comparing to the last nuance husbands, dates and attentive strangers.

Of twelve I did not know who was worst. Their desks a mess, drawers needed prying open from a fill of salves snacks sanitary napkins. Similar in laziness they would tell their classes what assignment to turn to, explain little if anything and leave them on their own, unconcerned if they understood what to do or not. Desk to desk I went to not leave them abandoned.

Three years went by this way. I took two courses fall and spring, two more in summer with an accelerated two-week class thrown in, sleeping little for all I was given to read.

I was half through college but what could college get a Black graduate: civil service work or teaching at a Black school which I was doing for all practical purposes and worn thin from. While the gang of twelve sat back I went about classes spoonfeeding coaxing correcting. The few male teachers at Clemmens plodded along like dobbins heading a cart down a cobbled lane. Some were so spiritless that reading the newspaper was the only pleasure of their day and told me so.

My fourth year at Clemmens I was sent to work in fifth and sixth grades where boys did just about what they wanted to. Sending them to Principal Rathfurd only emboldened them more. A note home meant nothing. To this day I don't understand how you can tell an 11 or 12-year-old, 15 nay 50 times a day to take a seat and stop preventing others from learning – and he will *not* have it. I would point, '*Will* you sit down and be quiet? Have you no shame?' And he would plop down and say 'No, I ain't.' I grew hoarse contending with these noisemakers teachers pretended not to notice.

They had been talking about a strike since the first week. March they refused the city's offer and voted to go out. The good economy meant it would not be easy to find replacements. Most college graduates were working. The school district posted in Sunday's newspaper for any college graduate. A posting next Sunday offered $50 a day. A week before the strike date there still wasn't enough response and an ad was placed to recruit school aides with a minimum sixty hours credit at a Kentucky college. I had more than sixty. If the strike took the rest of the school year I could make $2500, a sum I had never imagined to have.

Monday I left Clemmens at noon, took a bus downtown and bought a transcript of my grades for a dollar. I walked four blocks to the Louisville School District building, interviewed by a counselor who approved me on the spot. There was one condition. Aides as replacement teachers could work only in their schools. Surely district administrators knew such aides would be scourged by faculty on their return.

'You want the position or not?'

I half heard.

'You're getting Miss Jones' fifth grade class. You know her?'

'Yes, I was assigned to her a few times.'

Of the glamour girls she was the most impatient, a man-hungry woman with temper to match. She had public shouting matches with Principal Rathfurd, the most scandalous in the main hall when he called her a streetwalker and she him a child molester.

I determined to make $50 a day as long as I could and take the consequences. Likely I would need to transfer but that was fine by me. The counselor took an emergency credential from the desk and typed my name to it. Going out on the front walk I got the notion to avoid pickets by getting to school early and leaving out back. They would see me only lining up the class at first bell and noontime when I took them to the cafeteria. I did the same as an aide. In class it would be a matter of finding enough readers to go around. A reader chock full of stories is essential. A teacher who has this has everything. No other text is needed. Arithmetic spelling science can be taught on the blackboard and I suspect is done so in many places.

Teachers went out on Wednesday afternoon. Up before light Thursday morn I put a hot iron to shirt and pants, put on a necktie and fixed bread and jam with a cup of tea. Making a stop at a fruit market I got a man there to sell me forty bags a penny each, then turned into an alley behind Clemmens Avenue to come up on the school from behind. Climbing the back fence I went to the boiler room doors. The school caretaker let me in. He had it good in a hideaway office, hardly more to do than keep the temperature in the building and send two custodians out to sweep, calling himself engineer in the deal. Pegging me for a scared rabbit, there was no fooling a blue collar Irishman with a coffee mug in his paw. I would have liked to see how bold he would be breaking a strike.

Rooms wide open I went to 24 with double windows to the ceiling. It lacked nothing but care. Teachers and custodians at Clemmens held a feud that custodians called professional jealousy. Teachers claimed custodians whisked through rooms doing little or nothing and custodians said teachers left a mess. Both were right. The truth was neither needed the other's help, one was lazier than the other and in a given instance it could be hard to tell who.

I counted the packet of class cards, 19 girls 16 boys, a good sign. A fifth grade class with more girls than boys is better behaved. I doubted 35 would arrive. Some would use the strike as an excuse not to come. I went through their desks, five rows of seven, piling everything on top. Seventeen readers turned up. No more would mean sharing which started quarrels about who would share with whom. I extracted some spellers and other texts. All else: candy gadgets old school work went into a paper bag.

Looking through Miss Jones' desk I found emory boards pantyhose hair spray skin cream Kotex pistachio nuts. From the bottom drawer I confiscated two packs of pencils. The sharpener in a corner had no handle but a crayon nub through the crank turned it. I wiped tatters of writing from the blackboard, wiped dust and debris from the window ledge, used the pole standing in a corner to open the over windows to let in fresh air. They screaked in that it had been quite some time. Glamour girl teachers do not like fresh air. No glamour girl ever liked fresh air. It bends stiff bouffant and dries moisturizer. Glamour girls require stuffiness which preserves moisture in skin.

The utility closet in back was locked. Risking another red Irish smirk I went to the boilers, found him sitting with his custodians, two louts who ogled teachers with sexual thoughts that could be read from down the hall. Taking a ring of keys that jingled like a tambourine one went with me.

It required a skeleton key and he went through them all before the lock turned. What I saw inside was a fire hazard and a shame to decency: books piled three feet high, lost clothing draped over brooms. Climbing atop I took two reams of paper and a box of chalk from a shelf. Next I dug through the pile finding twelve coverless readers, but the teacher I readied myself to be needed no covers on books. With the best of the brooms I swept the floor. Else patched windows it looked like a schoolroom for Norman Rockwell. Seven-thirty on the dot, twenty minutes before first bell, I lay down in a corner.

I awoke to the chirping of children on playground, a sound that carries two three city blocks spring morns. Going down to double doors on the side I looked out over a yard of gradeschoolers but saw no pickets at the gate. They should have been there by now but I knew not to underestimate their sloth.

Replacement teachers were down the hall. Leaning on their push brooms the two custodians looked over young white women come to teach. I wound through them into the office. The school secretary gave the emergency credential and me both a look. Given the room key I signed in Miss Jones' place. Attractive Miss Blevins, the vice principal, hurried by to pass out pencils and booklets on schedules and lesson plans. She didn't include me. I didn't need the booklets. I could have used more pencils but anonymity would serve me better.

First bell rang. In five minutes I would be a teacher at age twenty. Following replacements to the side doors, I slipped out behind them. Pickets were at the parking gate waiting for Principal Rathfurd who was late, emptyhanded they were as signs were late, too. I went to the line-up mark for Room 24.

A girl came, 'Are *you* going to teach us?'

At the bell I herded them. Girls moving up slowly, by pure will I got the boys in line. On the way in I saw replacements unable to assemble their classes.

Upstairs they entered 24 thinking goodies bags had been prepared. Finding their junk they squealed. I would have none of it, passing out pencils, telling them to write their names on the bags. Collecting I locked them in the closet. Stuck with a reader, brand new pencil, the strength of my will, they seemed taken, especially girls in front who proved to be hungry learners.

I said we'd start with vocabulary, and as they reached for spellers I said it wasn't necessary. Instead of twenty words a week they would get twenty a day. I wrote them on the board, all associated with the classroom: *pencil paper eraser chalk ruler board, etc.* I told them as fifth graders it was important that they know how to use these words in talking writing.

Standing up one at a time to recite from the board some were still not readers but the words were allied and familiar. Those who stumbled told to recite again, for them it wasn't so much reading as recognition but that was fine for now. I was mainly interested in class flow.

Telling them they would never really know a word until they practice writing it – making corrolaries up as I went – I passed out paper and had them write each word ten times, five across twice.

I went about correcting writing printing too large small slanted crooked. It is not hard to improve handwriting. It may be the lightest thing to teach gradeschoolers. The trick is to get it into their heads that the easier it is to read the better.

I took the red crayon nub and went desk to desk putting a grade mark on each paper. For a capper I tore sheets of paper in half across a ruler, passed them out and had lines numbered 1 to 20 for a quiz – I to point to a classroom object, they to write the word from the board that named it. Waiting with stopped breath as I pointed to the sharpener, a pencil ruler eraser . . . they quickly wrote and covered their answers. Collecting papers I marked a red *A* for a perfect score, which all were but two. Girls in front thought the quiz simple but for now I had to give the class a feeling of unity. I had them sit back a minute. No one came late and there wasn't a noisemaker in the room. The boys were followers. They went with class leaders good or bad. Were there a renegade they would have taken up with him.

I took attendance of 28 and hung the cards in a pouch out on the door. Telling them to open their readers I picked out a story on trailblazers of the American West to read aloud. Those who barely read I coaxed word to word, sound by sound. No one was brushed off and they saw I would let no one fall away. More importantly the story interested them. We discussed what trailblazers ate, where they slept, how they stayed warm and healed wounds.

Passing out more half sheets I printed TRUE or FALSE on the board, then spoke ten statements on the story for them to yes or no. Again they enjoyed it.

Morning done I lined them up in the hall for lunch. Downstairs and out through double doors to the yard we came up behind other classes. Along the fence Clemmens teachers cursed replacements, the usually timid white librarian climbing half over. Supposed educated individuals screamed like a violent mob. I loathe mobs of any size, all with royal blood do.

Moving the class to lunch, my name was called out but not cursed which meant the teachers still took me for an aide. Sending them into the cafeteria I could have gone to the teachers lounge and listened to replacements tell each other what they had experienced but was of mind the less anyone laid eyes on me the better. I went up to 24 cheerful I just made $25 in a few hours, a few more to make it fifty, thrilled to remain so inconspicuous that Clemmens teachers would not know I profited in their absence until I was gone.

Beating the second lunch bell to the double doors I saw strikers had cleared away, gone for their own lunch. My girls lined up, boys coming up behind. Other fifth and sixth grade classes were scattered. Replacements looked my way but it was too early for jealousy, only the first day, but it would come. Back in class I guessed even the slowest could add a few numbers. Needing to be sure to bring them along I called them up two at a time, their backs to the board while I put identical additions on the board, five single-digit numbers to be added up, the answer 45 or less.

The first two whirled around, the winner clapping her answer on, leaving the other breathless. Calling the rest, matching winners until two were left, I took a quarter from my pocket and put it out. There was a hush: a quarter bought a local soft drink or bag of chips.

The winner nearly broke her glasses getting her answer up. Cheers were earsplitting. I passed out paper to be folded in half four times over, grooving sixteen squares on one side sixteen on the other, numbered across 1-16 in front, 17-32 in back. Numbering 32 additions on the board to be copied accordingly to each square, I gave them forty minutes to work, then graded each paper using red crayon to mark scores.

Even for an experienced teacher it is not easy to keep a class strong through the last hour. Many a teacher loses hold. I got an old globe from the back and gave a geography lesson off the top of my head, showing there was far more water than land yet explaining an old sailor lament: water water everywhere, not a drop to drink – which they didn't believe.

I showed them blue rivers lakes we drank from and pointed to Kentucky and Louisville and where grandmothers and cousins lived as they called out cities. A half hour to go they asked to go out and play, but that would put me out on the yard while strikers were forming up again to harass replacements on leaving. Instead I sent Brenda, my lead girl and winner of the quarter, down to Custodial for the key to the library. Because the librarian was out screaming with teachers didn't mean the library should be closed. The library was for students not librarians, an idea you might not get by the stingy way they parceled out time to come in. In their meek way these school librarians were more loath to trouble themselves with children than all the rest.

I knew she would return with the key. She had gone with single purpose and would not take no for an answer could she help it. She was my lead girl and sat with three others like her in front. It was a crime of negligence with the black community to blame that girls like them were not nurtured. Hungry to learn they leaned up for every word. Thin plain all four, unfanciful of clothes and boys, valuing neither hairstyles nor heartthrobs, they wore hand me downs their mothers had worn. Minds clear there was little of good learning they would be unable to put to use – task and duty to give them enough. That these girls and many more like them are not brought along speaks of worthless teachers and administrators. That they do not grow to become physicians teachers community leaders speaks of sloth and irresponsibility by the black community. White people are not partly to blame here. They have their own problems and not everything is so hunky-dory on their side. First you see to your own, everybody knows that.

I passed out the bags to take home. The girls asked if there was homework and I made up another corollary: a good schoolday requires no homework. They whooped for it rang true.

Leading them downstairs like taking them out to play I saw no one of consequence in the hall and veered them into the library, the day made. I sat at Mrs. Kilfon's desk as they browsed shelves and brought me books, wanting to learn more.

At 2:25 I had them before the double doors. Strikers lined the fence, their spouses double-parked blocking the street. Replacements would be unable to get away until authorities came. With no car it was not my concern. I was leaving over the fence in back. I would go up to the room, write a plan for Friday, sign out and be gone. The bell rang and I let them go. Upstairs I went with library key in hand where it would stay until the end of the strike, not that the custodians would miss it.

Same time next morn I went in through the back and put twenty words on the board linked with arm and leg: shoulder to fingertip, hip to heel; *elbow, wrist, thumb, palm, knuckle, ankle, thigh, knee, shin.* . . . Fast to them even boys sat up straight. After recitation I gave a quiz pointing here there on myself.

Next we read and discussed a story on the great Negro cowboy Nat Love. Were he a white man, I said, his name would stand with legends they knew from Saturday morning TV shows.

After lunch they got another 32 additions, this time numbers of two digits that carried to a third. It was too easy for the girls but they knew I was leading to something. With an hour to go I gave them a lesson in dollars and cents. Displaying a dollar and coins from my pocket I showed on the board how to punctuate money, sending them up one at a time to print an amount I called out, like $1.28. It was not as easy for them to get as I thought it would be. New to translating a sound to a dollars cents number it took awhile even for the lead girls to pick up but all in class were keen to the utility.

Again we went down to library where they were noisy but it was Friday, after all. Through the shades I saw strikers lining up outside the fence. At the double doors I let the class go, no one catching a glimpse of me. I went back up to the room, another $50 to the ledger for what seemed to be no more than a half day's work.

Taking a sheet of paper I planned Monday. It took twenty minutes no more but looking through the reader I saw a problem coming. Only eight nine more stories would interest them. These fifth graders were in class 180 days a year and needed a new four five six-page story each and every day. How can so many fit into a reader? Possibly one twice taller twice wider thrice thicker. It would not be unwieldy, merely made harder to disappear, misplace, or for the administration to misdistribute as usually happens to parts of shipments meant for poor schools.

Most suit running done by noon Saturdays it was custom for runners to meet at a Greek counter for a plate of lamb. Two dollars for a lamb leg, potatoes and carrots always too steep for me, that Saturday I determined I owed myself a plate and took a bus downtown. Only six runners left they knew their jobs were not long to go.

Back to school Monday morn I passed the boilers and Irish smirk. I had twenty words for the board, a story picked out to read, three-digit numbers to add, and a practical life lesson to end the day. Out on the yard I counted only four strikers at the fence. Replacements stood at their marks faced with classes they couldn't control. I wanted to give no reason to be approached. It is common in grade school for a stronger teacher to accept a weaker teacher's *noisemaker* for 'babysitting,' the term *troublemaker* proscribed by the downtown office. One or two in a room stop the learning endeavor; three four turn a class to chaos.

Twenty new words were learned to start the morn, Monday: common tools and utensils, Tuesday: fruits and vegetables, Wednesday: farm animals and their young. Their reading improved on three American legends: Monday, six pages about Amelia Earhart they took more interest in than I thought they would; Tuesday, the story of John Henry and his hammer; Wednesday, Johnny Appleseed and the pot on his head. Asked if it were true I said a story that good must have truth. They worked more additions, getting another speed contest on the board. They would soon start multiplication which I planned to make them good at in no time, proclaiming that everything to learn in math past fifth grade: fractions percentages decimals and, further on, algebra geometry would depend on knowing how to multiply, and if they didn't learn how they couldn't learn what followed. The girls in front wanted at it.

Thursday morn as I stepped out on the yard two replacements were straight to.

'Could we ask you something?' The lead kept her distance – a sign someone wants something but keeps you at arm's-length as a lesser person.

'Are you teacher or aide?'

'I worked as an aide.' I measured my words. 'I took over on an emergency basis.'

'You have sixty or more credits?'

'Yes.'

'That makes you a teacher.'

I did not reply.

'What's your secret? Our classes are so wild. Is there something you can suggest?'

'Have a good story every day to read and discuss, give a quiz and grade it right then. It gives the idea reading is useful and rewarding.'

'Half our classes can't read.'

'Stand them up, read with them once twice thrice; they start to recognize words.'

I should have said no more.

'For spelling give twenty a day, twenty that go together like classroom items or everyday verbs.'

She looked puzzled. 'Aren't you going by the lesson plan booklet?'

'I didn't get one,' I winked. 'I know what these classes need to do just from being here three and a half years.'

She half introduced herself. 'I'm Becky; that's Cheryl.' Her friend was to the point.

'We have boys who probably need a little male supervision. Could we send them to you afternoons?'

I too to the point, 'I can't take them. Boys in my class will go to their side and learning will be thrown off.'

'You know,' she said, 'the district recommends —'

'I won't have them.'

She turned away like it was not her idea to approach me in the first place. They came to me for no other reason than to palm off their noisemakers.

At last bell I took the class down to the double doors for dismissal. Brenda and a friend pointed down the hall to their mothers there to see Principal Rathfurd. Usually when a teacher hears this it makes for a restless night. I knew they had something good to say but the attention coming my way would do me none.

Friday as I took the class through new words, Popinjoy the school lackey came to the door and told me to see Principal *Sir*. He didn't call Principal Rathfurd by name because he was missing front teeth and *Rathfurd* came out a vulgarity to the delight of teachers, especially glamour girls.

The school secretary told me to go in. Rathfurd had not greeted me in my three and a half years there.

'Two mothers came sayin' they want you to take over. What kind of hoodoo you workin'?'

He knew I was Haitian and word had been around that Haitian fortune tellers next to a burlesque hall had wiped his eyes clean to the tune of $1000. Since then he bore all Haiti a grudge.

'I give lessons in reading writing and numbers.'

'You followin' LSD schedule? Replacements say you're doin' your own thing. Bring no half-baked mumbo jumbo how to teach school. I'll put you out. Those mothers were rappin' my desk. Cause me no more crap here. Send Popinjoy back.'

Returned to the room I relieved Popinjoy. So was the comical perception of him that the ten minutes I was away threw the class off serious thought. I had to bear down to get them back on course, myself too, disillusioned to be where accomplishment was rebuked not rewarded. I never thought this could be in this good land America, well near my deepest belief.

Taking the class to the lunch line I saw a reporter and her photographer among the pickets, jacket skirt blouse awave with chestnut hair. When I went back out for them she was inside the fence with the two replacements who had approached me. Breaking away she made straight across.

'Excuse me, you're a replacement teacher?'

'I'm in charge of a class.'

'Ilene Weitz with the *Post*. What's been your experience here?'

'It's been good.'

'I was told you have good control of your class.'

'I work as an aide and have experience.'

My legs could not turn away at the ring of the bell.

'May I observe your class?'

I braved her eyes. 'Miss Weitz, I'd appreciate you leaving me out of your report. After strike replacements will be gone, I'll still be here to face the teachers. Would it be smart to call attention to myself?'

Day done I sat savoring $350 I had coming, reviewing what was accomplished in seven days. We had become acquainted with 140 words, each written ten times with instruction as to proper size and slant. We had read aloud and discussed seven stories that would stick with them the rest of their lives as a good grade school story will . . .

Peeking through the door, a wiley principal it is who won't enter a schoolroom until he looks it corner to corner. Mr. Rathfurd brought in the *Post* reporter.

'Miss Weitz wants to hear about your replacement experience. Tell her what she needs to know.'

She brought in her photographer as though my rejection of her request meant nothing. Rathfurd left closing the door behind him.

'May I sit?'

She took a front desk and looked around.

'It's been awhile.'

The photographer snapping pictures from all around, I turned over my shoulder and he snapped one of my face. Caring not for his airs I advised myself he was doing his job.

'Your name?' she asked.

'Daupin Capet.'

'*Daupin?*'

'Yes, French, a form of *Dauphin*.'

'You're a college graduate?'

'I have enough college to take a class.'

'Whose class?'

'Miss Jones was teacher here.'

'You said you're concerned about facing the regular teachers after the strike?'

'I am.'

'Why'd you take a class?'

I thought how to answer. 'You might say I have the lay of the land with more right to one than a newcomer. Too, I have always considered a job a friend, any job at all – well, *almost* any.'

'Will you say that to Miss Jones and other teachers when the strike is over?'

'I'm more concerned with what they'll have to say – Miss Weitz, I like to co-operate but I said outside I don't want to be part of your report. You forced your way in behind

Principal Rathfurd and when this is all over the replacements will be gone never to be seen again and I'll be here to be ostracized by the faculty. How would you feel if I sat there with pen and pad to cause you a good deal of trouble?'

Seemingly reconsidering, she told the photographer to wait for her in the car. He didn't think it a good idea but she insisted. Slouching a little she rolled her neck like I were not there. I wondered why she didn't leave with him.

'Your job isn't so easy?' I posed with an inkling she might be impressed with me.

'Not as easy as it looks.'

She took off her jacket over a sleeveless blouse, showing armpits so hollow they looked like sexual parts. I did not need to steal a look at her athletic legs – she displayed them. My eyes would not have their fill.

'And you?' she asked. 'Will you get accreditation to become a teacher?'

'I don't know if teaching can hold me. I watch how things are done and oft see a better way. Just about everything I start on I see a better way.'

'Have you seen a better way to teach?'

'One needn't look hard.'

'Oh?'

'I have girls in front where you sit – school is the light of their day. There is no limit to how much they could learn if taught smartly.'

'What do you mean?'

'Sensible progressive accumulation building like change in a jar. I would guess you have a sharp eye, Miss Weitz, you were smart through school and never let grass grow under your feet; but these girls would have been your match.'

'Why so?'

'You can't compare other fifth-graders to them. They have seen things they shouldn't see, faced dangers and developed instinct and judgment even white adults don't have; and they are so acute by this that white students don't compare to them. And schools, instead of bending their backs a bit, will let these girls go to become young mothers, and let's face it that's what they'll be not long from now – all because of the indifference of those who put themselves before education of children.'

'Two mothers told me their girls have learned more in your class than they have all year.'

It struck me odd she withheld that, seeming it would have been a good way to start. Yet I thrilled my work was approved.

'Does that go for all teachers here?' she kept on.

'A few teach. To most of them it's a day's pay and opportunity to show off shoes and outfits. Most of all they care about their nails and what snacks are brought. It's shameful they have the audacity to go on strike and want more money and early tenure.'

'Why shameful?'

'The individual counts not tenure. From what I've seen all you need to teach is ability to explain in a clear concise way something you know to somebody who doesn't – and who doesn't know more than a fifth grader? With sixty some college hours I've had no trouble. I don't mind making $50 a day on the teachers. I have never seen such money. I hope the strike goes to summer.'

'So teachers are the problem?'

'And principals. Many probably get the job because they are good at looking out for themselves and when you look out mainly for yourself how can you see to children?'

'So it's teachers and principals?'

'One more.'

'Which is?'

'I said there are always lead girls in class; there are also lead boys – *noisemakers* we're told to call them – who have other boys following. They cause disruption all day but are hardly punished. Most of the teacher's attention goes to them. They are coddled and bribed.'

'What should be done?'

'They should not be in a proper class. They should not be allowed to be where eager learning takes place. They get in the way. Put them somewhere, collect them if need be.'

'Where?'

'I don't *care* where. I'm not sentimental about them. One hit me on the head with a pear as hard as a rock from a third floor window. I was knocked unconscious delivering a note. I say put them where they can drive each other crazy —'

My mouth yet half full she stood up in my eyes, put on her jacket and bid me good day.

On the bus going downtown I recalled every word gesture exhalation passing between us, speaking to myself like a suitor rethinking his lines, seeing where I could have said better. For the first time in night classes I sat with divided attention.

I returned to the gully still imbued with her every word and gesture. Rarely did I let my mind wander freely or look idly about. I thought it no good in the long run, but now I beat back and forth in the trailer allowing I was two-legged, meeting her not as replacement teacher but battle-hardened correspondent with a way about me, and she a daring tyro. I forced myself to lie down or walk through the night. I had spoken my mind – perhaps too much so – but she seemed taken. Anticipating she would contact me, wanting to introduce me to vital educators, I saw myself telling them just what I told her – something one way or another sure to come of our talk.

Getting a late start I went downtown to find a day's work. Savile Row mostly closed for a Jewish holiday, I went to a shoe store owned by a young Greek, the type of proprietor who works in a mess yet knows where everything is. Shoe boxes piled in front and rear I cleared two areas and stacked together all alike by size, the difference there like from night and day. He paid $11, $2.20 an hour, $2.20 an hour more than I would have made in the trailer thinking about Ilene Weitz.

Sunday Easter and Jewish Holiday both, I went down Freeman Road to Yank's. With Granme gone I paid $2 for a haircut like everybody else unless I would rather pay 50 cents at Downtown Barber College, which was hit or miss. You could walk out there looking an escaped fugitive. Seating myself I reached over to *Louisville Sunday Post*:

STRIKE OVER!

Needless excitement I'd allowed myself about it going to summer and making $2500 was put out like a candle by a spout. Agreement made giving teachers much of what they asked for with LTU to vote on it that eve, spokesmen on both sides said there was no winner because teaching children had been disrupted. Overleaf I turned to a photo of the two replacements who approached me, reading that both agreed their experience at Samuel Clemmens was rewarding and they had formed emotional ties to their classes, but said the teachers were needed back. I did not finish their lies for I stiffened at what looked like a thief in a store looking over his shoulder before he steals. Followed in thick print:

SUB SCOFFS TEACHERS

A Clemmens replacement who does not believe regular teachers are missed is Daupin Capet, a teacher's aide who took over Miss Jones' fifth grade class.

"They come in like it's a fashion show," he said in one on one conversation. "They are more concerned about their nails than children."

81

Daupin believes tenure is not necessarily merit. "To teach you only need know more than they do. Who doesn't know more than fifth graders?"

He is of the opinion that admimistrators are rather too busy seeing to themselves than to children, and that rambunctious boys take over classrooms and teachers and administrators cater to them. "These boys," he said, "should be collected and put where they can drive each other crazy." He speaks of experience, having been knocked cold by one.

He likes $50 a day replacement pay, adding he has never seen such money and hopes the strike drags on to summer. *Ilene Weitz*

Forenoon through eve I imagined individuals I didn't even know laying for me. Concerned naught about the male teachers – little more were they than walking dead – I sensed no danger from them. Sex-starved women I feared, glamour girls who hoarded vitriol for confrontations with men, enjoying them like sexual couplings. Ten weeks to summer vacation, I advised myself I had gone through worse but could think of no excuse to tell them for my scabbing. Everything I thought to say, on reconsideration, would make them only more angry. It came to me to tell them I had to pay for a burial – though Granme passed four years before.

Getting to Clemmens half past seven, I climbed over the back fence. The Irish man's wink let me know he had read Sunday's paper. Afoot on newly buffed floor I felt like I'd been away a year not a weekend. Two of the better teachers, Mrs. Ross and Mrs. Strong, were in the office. A coy good morn bid me I signed in and exchanged keys.

Opening the Special Education room I sat down at the center table estimating the retribution coming – a week of it, a month? First bell Mrs. Billups came in wearing a spring pantsuit.

'Morning, Daupin.'

'Good morn, Mrs. Billups, welcome back.'

She put her jacket in the closet, looked about and sat down. Spreading her *Louisville Post* flat on the table she peered over her glasses.

'I understand you took a class.'

'Miss Jones', I had enough college units to be paid as a teacher.'

'I heard mothers demanded you take over.'

'Oh, I was going on pure energy, I'm not a finished educator.'

Her lips purring *'Ahhhhum,'* she turned a page.

Special education teachers were not required to assembly. We remained sitting. A third grade girl came and read with me, then came a second grade boy I helped with numbers until 9:45.

Mrs. Billups went on her break. Returned she said there were refreshments in the lounge. I doubted she would steer me into danger. Could it be teachers weren't angry? Getting what they wanted, out just long enough for a nice break, did they hear what Room 24 accomplished and feel school spirit? I was after all one of the staff.

Teachers lounge was in a wing of the main building, opening to playground. I looked slowly about. It seemed every woman teacher but Mrs. Billups was there, done up heels to hair. I saw not a man. Vegetable sticks and crowns were dipped devoured, diets begun along with the new contract. Else Miss Jones in bright red all went still. Hemmed in she hissed my name with vile sexual epithets. If that was not enough warning to turn right around I don't know what but I wanted to have it over with.

Mrs. Beauchamp, married to a lawyer and the most conceited teacher at Clemmens, acknowledged my presence.

'Daupin, *no?*'

'Yes.'

'Since you're the only male here – you *are* a male form of some species?'

'Yes.'

'Will you open the pink box so we can have something with coffee?'

Vulgar names still coming, glamour girls crowded up. I picked up kindergarden scissors and cut the string, lifting the lid on an old work boot in a bed of parsley, the type you see thrown away in an alley, odder yet a brick stuffed inside.

Wondering what's the meaning of this a shriek half human half horn pierced my ears – this followed by clicks of a spike heel, but only one, as Miss Jones ran up from behind and let me have it over the back of the head. Set upon I slipped to all fours. Punched kicked stomped, through it all came Mrs. Beauchamp, *'Get him, girls! Get him good!'* They tried to get me around the head but I rolled under the table against the wall. Ducking hefty nyloned feet I hung from the crossbar so it wouldn't overturn. Swung in by the rawhide laces the bricked boot clouted my skull. They would have flushed me out had not good Popinjoy run in.

'In the *name* of Jesus! In Jesus Lord's name!'

Through a gap between their hips and legs I ran on my knees for the double doors. Barging out on the yard I hotfooted across asphalt covering ground. Haste carried me over a six-foot fence.

On a bus downtown, the top of my head felt cracked. Finding a pay phone I called the school district, remembering who accredited me as a teacher.

'Mr. Phipps, Daupin Capet, you signed me as a replacement at Clemmens Elementary.'

'Yeh?'

'I was physically assaulted, I need to transfer.'

'Get a letter from the principal.'

'Mr. Rathfurd is an aloof man. In all my time as an aide he has hardly said a word to me.'

'You need his recommendation.'

'He will not do this for me. Is there another way?'

'District policy so another school won't get a dud.'

I was sure district employees got around much policy but bloodless bureaucrat Mr. Phipps would not let it pass.

I was left now with the idea of bottling a hair potion Granme made up in the compound. She had mixed urine with vinegar, simple enough, but it had to be urine of an old coot whose vital minerals were leaving his body. Hair grower ads in back of magazines would not keep showing up but for those who were ready to try remedy after remedy, call themselves fools yet still hold forth for any and all popping up anew. To start I would have to take it door to door but I never any day suffered from shyness, the handicap that keeps more individuals from wealth and vital life experience than any other. Clear enough it was but where could I find raw product? I could go to a hospice and ask attendants to collect urine, yet how many times before they deemed me a pain?

I recalled a hunchback in a cubbyhole in the alley behind Savile Row who did overflow for suit sellers. Mel sent me to him with pinned suits when Nate's hands were full. Oft I waited. Called Nate, too, he drank tea as he worked. Either he didn't have privy or didn't waste time to go to one but would pull out *putz* he called it that belonged on a man twice his size – it is an old Haitian saying God does not strike with both hands – and with no beg your pardon let go a rail of orange into a pail, that glowed in the darkness there.

Sitting under a lamp ten hours, his diet cold chicken and pickles with the tea, he certainly emptied a gallon in that pail every day. Collecting it on the way home at night would take explaining. Old Jews with accents took little at face value. He would want to know why and like my teacher Nate, Yiddish hunchbacks were sharp as tacks when they inquired about your motives.

Truth be told I would give away the most sought after concoction in the world – a true hair fertilizer. My nature truthful, truthful nature harms more oft than not. No common fellow climbs heights without deceits. An individual on the rise should not lie outright but must weigh and measure what truth he allows. I would say I need fertilizer for a pepper patch, no other pretext for handling raw urine could I expect him to believe.

It required now I not be timid about going to a man I little knew for *pishachts*, he called it, from the pail, a man who had not been friendly, even intimating black people's ignorances that showed he thought himself better.

Morn at Army Surplus on Fourth Street I purchased a jerry can and a funnel. Going to Savile Row into the alley, I saw his sign still up.

At the machine as always, a lamp over, pail aside, he swiveled around.

'What's in your hand?'

'Nothing.' I shook it.

'Why did you bring this here?'

'Remember me? I ran suits for Mel. I have a little gully to grow peppers. Could I stop by a few times a week to pour out from your pail for fertilizer? That would save you dumping it.'

He looked frightened. 'Why come to me? Why not use yours? What is special about mine?'

'The urine must be rich with color. This comes from an older man.'

'You want this to pour in your garden?'

'Yes.'

'Sounds fishy. What peppers need this?'

'Haitian peppers grow best from rich urine. I sell them on the side of the road.'

86

'This is how you make money?'

'Recently I was a teacher.'

'You?'

'During the strike.'

He shook his head. 'Why not? Black people can do this.'

I nodded to the pail. 'May I?'

'I know people who plant. I want to hear what they say.'

'Let me save you the trouble of throwing it out.'

'Come back.'

Seeing about a container I looked over hair creams, most of them tubed now, a few still in glass. When a schoolboy I walked alleys finding items to bring to Granme. I recalled a place near the tracks called PDQ Whiskey, a sneaky Pete of whisky oil and quick alcohol sold around Louisville and Southern Indiana to down and out Negroes and white cheapskates. No Negro with the price of a better bottle would have it. Cartons of bottles on which labels were creased or miscentered were left on the side of the dock. Peddlers with horse carts came for them. Once, I took home a box, could find no use for the bottles and discarded them.

Off the bus at Cold Avenue I went into the alley and rang the bell to the back entrance. A heavy gate rolled up on two men, one in overalls.

'I used to see boxes with empty bottles back here. Do you have any I could take off your hands?'

I thought I would be told to move on, but he in overalls brought four boxes on a dolly, half pints, 24 in a box with no caps. I didn't have it in me to ask if they had any to spare. Taking the boxes off the dock I carried them two at a time to the corner to await a bus.

Bringing them to the gully I took a single bottle back on the bus to a cork company near downtown. A receptionist called out a management fellow in white shirt and tie; these fellows found in any company of size are obliging if it's no skin off the nose.

'I need corks to stop this size bottle.'

We went to the back and tried two, first too tight, second snug.

'We sell by the thousand.'

'I'm starting a small business. Could you sell me a hundred?'

'I'll split a box by sight. I won't count 'em.'

I bought half a box for $10.

Stopping at a counter I worked out a label with the title: *Hair Grower #9*, after the popular American teenager song *Love Potion #9* that played years on radio in Haiti – a song with the soul of a Haitian. I drew *HG#9* inside a circle cradled by subtitle: *Ancient Hair Grower*. At the bottom *I put Daupin Mfg, Louisville, Kentucky.*

I took design and bottle to a downtown printer and another of those management fellows told me he had a label to cover the PDQ label, 250 for $25, and would typeset a fancy design for $20 more.

Not counting the design each label cost a dime, 2 pennies a cork, bottles free and if Nate let me empty the bucket three four times a week I would have my company.

Not wanting to risk his mood too early, I arrived midmorn with jerry can and funnel. He looked back.

'You want my pishachts? Take it, you shit.'

Without a word, not even 'thanks,' I put the funnel in the container and poured in his waste.

He stood up, pulling out putz. 'Want more?'

I would not stand there and accommodate him urinating into the bucket.

Returned to the gully I added a pint of cider vinegar. Morn I put on Granme's rubber gloves, put the funnel into the bottles, filled 24 – pouring out rosy – and corked them.

A bottle in my hip pocket I rode the bus back downtown getting off on Liberty Road and going to the printer, who showed me red lettering over sepia. Placed over the white

PDQ label it tuned with the rosy bottle. Taking the labels back I stuck them on and stood back for a look at my first box of product.

Morn in shirt and tie I rode the bus with the box on my lap, going to a real estate office where the secretary was always cheerful when I delivered Mel's suits.

'Good morn, Mrs. Ryan.'

'Daupin, right? Where did you go?'

'I went to college a few years.'

'A few years! What're you doing with all that knowledge?'

She was one of those abstemious hollow-cheeked Southern Christian women with legs like a racehorse. If her cheer didn't get you the legs did the trick.

'I sell a hair grower. If a head hasn't lost too much it will grow a patch.'

'You don't say?'

I gave her a bottle. 'An old Haitian tonic. Do you know someone losing hair?'

'My husband.'

'Please have it.'

'Really?'

For her welcome and friendliness I counted it a sale because of an old Creole saying: a good thing in good hands bodes good all around.

'Have him rub in a handful, put on a shower cap and the pressure from the gas opens pores and fertilizes the scalp.'

Out came Mr. Hannum. 'What's that, snake oil?'

She handed it to him. 'Daupin used to bring your suits. Now he has a tonic that grows hair.'

His scalp receded in wingtip fashion, potion would not help there but a combed-over spot in back looked like it could be fertilized.

'This a whisky bottle?'

'Old-time look to lend to the idea,' I explained.

Pulling the cork he winced.

'*What's* in here?'

'Powerful natural product.'

'What price?'

Mr. Hannum, downtown civic leader, bought two suits a year. Certainly he went by the credo you get what you pay for. Would I lower expectation by saying a dollar? I left with my first $2, believing hair would grow out on his head and word of mouth would get to city bigwigs and possibly Louisville's mayor who looked to be thinning in photos.

I went to a lawyer on the second floor, a man six foot ten inches tall who had played college basketball for Kentucky and gone on to the Syracuse Nationals of the professional league. He was the tallest man I'd ever seen, his hair blond and crinkly. Old office with rail, his secretary, no spring chicken, had most of it to herself. Mr. Kuehn's desk was in a walled corner. Stepping out in shirtsleeves his head was near the ceiling.

'What can I do you for?'

'I used to deliver suits to you.' I took a bottle from the box.

'I sell a true hair fertilizer called HG9.'

'A what?'

'It grows hair.'

'Move on, fella.'

The old girl cackling I went out in the hall for a talk with myself. I could not let myself get excited by an easy sale nor discouraged by a mean snub. Both had to be fairly dissipated by the time I stepped away. I looked at the bottle, the label I thrilled over. From what I'd read in *Reader's Digest*, each door to door product from hairbrushes to vacuum cleaners sold at a certain rate per hundred calls. It might be two or five but these percentages are realized over time. This figure established, the groundwork of my business would be a core of customers ordering weekly which would bring income to use for advertisement and eventual distribution from warehouse to stores and shops.

Through four more doors I found no buyers. Back on the ground floor I stepped into an optical company. A sign read no solicitors but in salesmen stories I had perused that was *good* not bad. Met by a Jewish face at the counter, I'd begun to recognize Jews in that they had faces like you saw in picture book bibles. Red hair furrowed over the top, most of it curled to the sides, he needed my product before it was too late.

'What's that?'

'Potion for growing hair. It is used with success in Haiti. Should a man start to lose, HG9 will grow it back.'

Lifting the cork his eyes grew.

'What's in here?'

'Natural carbon nitrogen potion first used by camel drivers in the East, come to the New World in Haiti. If it grows you no hair you'll get your money back.'

He showed the bottle around in back.

'We'll try three.'

He paid $6 from an envelope in a drawer. Next building I walked in on a buisnessman leaning over his secretary with his cuffs out. When I held up a bottle he said he took no peddlers. Apparently he wanted to show her how he handled an intruder. I went next door into the same office. He reached for the telephone. Since being kicked by a Tonton Macoutte I feared all authorities but if I let him run me out of the building I might see reason to quit. I would finish there door to door even if it got me a police citation.

Police didn't come and I sold a bottle to a man in an untitled office who seemed to be sitting with nothing to do, amused he was by cork and label.

It did not take long to rethink my approach. Counting doors put one in a hurry to get to the next. Behind each was a

91

contest of will to represent against resistance to buy. I could not step back until it was no use. Later I stood against a gruff man on the street and wore him down. Then a polite man in a lobby asking question after question seemed sold before handing the bottle back. Nothing was sure but a percentage that worked itself out in time.

Selling five the first day I returned next morn to what remained of Savile Row. Of the suit sellers left only one bought a bottle. Midday, $2 to show for my walking, I followed an alleyway to a motor pool where men worked on city buses. Knowing I should not be there from a sign on the gate, halfway around I sold a bottle before being told to move on. That made $4 for the day and kept me going.

Hardly needing to I went to the gully for the jerry can and back on the bus to Nate for raw product. Stooped over his machine as always, I noticed his hands weakening as I had seen Granme's hands slipping off what they held. He greeted me as before. 'Come for *pishachts?* Take it, you shit.' This over the shoulder remark I attributed to his giving something away, even if it was his own waste. Without a second look he sat at his alterations, each bringing spirit of selling a skill piecemeal. In Haiti it is said the bitter go on, but as bitter as he was I didn't think he would be around too much longer.

Monday I walked in on Mrs. Ryan.

'Is it working?'

'Baby fuzz grew in! He's toting a mirror. He said to get another bottle, Mr. Hannum, too.'

I left with $4 and went down to the optical man on the ground floor. Bowing to show new fuzz in the furrow on his scalp he bought two more bottles.

Selling three to five a day, it would be like that I guessed until word of mouth built of the authenticity of HG9. I fell asleep thinking only of getting going again, bothered as an earlybird that a few hours of daylight were on my hands before most downtown offices and shops opened.

Friday the bus detoured from Freeman Road, descending a long hill to a drive-in theater turned into a junkyard for do-it-yourself mechanics to pick over with their own tools. They were let through the gate at seven to detach parts then bring them to a cashier and pay a standard price for each be it Cadillac or Chevrolet. The plaza in front had vendors selling everything from coffee and donuts to knives and belts under a lit marquee as though movies still played.

Since most arrivals wore caps I guessed who might be thinning, walking alongside to present a bottle and guarantee growth if a head had not lost too much. Touting the formula came originally from the Eastern Steppes where herdsmen lived over a hundred keeping a full head of hair, and that it would take but a week or two before they saw a little fuzz, I sold two bottles by nine.

Heading uphill I was cheered of good turns so far, like the detour. When I first went to PDQ they had only the half pint bottle to give. Of choice I would have taken the pint, a naïve notion, for a vendor who doesn't balance value and quantity won't be in business long no matter the product. Then at Downtown Real Estate if I hadn't had the voice to say $2, the proceeds would be half what they were – and price counted little. If HG9 worked it was worth fifty, nay a hundred times $2.

My check come from LSD in the mail, next morn I walked uphill from Take-A-Part and saw a sign on a red convertible, a small Pontiac in front of a residence off roadway terraced around the hill. Climbing over the rail I read the price, $350, the amount of the check. Looking inside at red bucket seats I recalled advice in *Reader's Digest* on used car buying: interior condition in a vehicle usually indicated its overall wear and tear.

I climbed steep stairs to a screen door. A man came out with keys and turned the ignition. Showing 60,000 miles which sounded like twice around the world to me, it had belonged to his brother who stripped it of trim and put a rack on the trunk to make it look like an English roadster.

Quitting early downtown to cash the check I returned to the terrace, climbed the stairs and said I had the money. Taking title and keys I left my purchase there and hiked down to Take-*A*-Part, recruiting a tow driver who swung uphill and hitched it to his truck.

Come to the gully owing him $10, I took a second notion as he unhooked. Carver's lot where I had gone to school was empty. I offered him $2 more to show me to tool around.

Putting the top down we spun out and swerved into the lot like to turn over. Taking the wheel I circled the paved surface, thrilled at the command at my hands. At almost all I could take he had me turn out on Freeman Road. Ahead a truck took its side and more. I meant to slide over but he yelled '*Straight!*' Swept by I dipped into the gully with no feeling left in hands and feet.

Still taking the bus downtown, on return to the gully I swung over to the Carver lot to wheel through staggered cardboard boxes I put out from behind the cafeteria, winding through them forward and in reverse. As with almost all I did I drew a point which was the quicker your eyes are front to rear, left to right, the more you see coming, and that is what roadway has to be about.

I took a booklet at the Motor Vehicles Office and memorized diagrams signs laws. Friday daybreak I drove there to be first in line to take a 30-question test. Finished I saw applicants spying each other's papers for better answers.

Bringing a tester to the roadster I turned out onto the street and drove him around the block expecting he would have me park four five different ways, but I needed do no more than pull to the curb before he sent me back. Always of mind I'd be well along before I got a car and license, I was taken inside to become a motorist not yet 21, no longer needing to get on a bus with a box of product, nor on Monday and Friday to double back to the gully for the jerry can to go collect raw material.

Spotting an ad for a downtown business service, $8 a month for a telephone number and up to fifty messages, I was given a number effective immediately. Going back to the printer I had a business card designed for *HG9*, undertitled: *Ancient Hair Grower Potion*.

I gave a card at all calls, selling a bottle or not. Now a customer needn't wait for me to come round. Six callers the first week, some didn't want delivery to a place of business but to a residence. Oft than not stood up at the door even though I was sure someone was inside, I determined to make it easier on myself. If not delivery to their work they could meet me at the donut shop at Third and Main where I sipped a cup of tea at the end of the day. Making a little office there I oft met with a customer or two.

I had my own domicile, my own business, two years of college, a red roadster, high time it was I found a companion. Risen in sleep I had two incidents like sensations of electrical current followed by a flash like in thunderous night, only to wake to a mess. I drove to Day & Night and purchased a thin top mattress. When it happened again on the new one I knew I had to get a female under my roof. A good few in Louisville needed one. I saw them downtown consorting with bums posing as hippies – is there any difference? Lean and arrogant they habitated in vans and had girls go begging change. Some looked as though they left good homes to be with longhaired loafers who spoke their own lingo and existed only to feel good, looking down on a responsible individual like myself. Of course that didn't stop them from sending naive girls to bring them coins so they could go to counters and buy workingman food. Some who took up with these bums were colored girls. Stopping to give a coin or two now and then, on one occasion I gave a dime. A beanpole over at the side of a building, resting a heel back on solid wall, let rip through his pants, adding *'Wow!'*

I developed a dislike for these exploiters, wanting to rescue these colored girls despoiling themselves with white good-for-nothings who passed gas at their pleasure, excusing themselves it is only natural to do so, that holding it in warped the system as rubber hose warps from hot water backing up in an engine block. I would have gladly informed each and all that if these emissions were for purpose of health, could they not simply step round the corner and expel privately not to demoralize those around them. I shamed for the girl, guessing she was of good family. Most colored girls who took up with hippies looked like they were.

A taxi company where Independence Road curved downtown had forty cabs in service daytime, twenty going nights, drivers on 12-hour shifts. Changeover between seven eight morn, drivers congregated in front with cigarettes coffee.

Turned into the lot, stepping out with a box of HG9 I happened upon a moocher calling himself Chicago who hounded me for a free sample with 'How'm I to know?'

'For $2 take a chance.'

'Let me rub in a handfull.'

He was thinning without much front recession, enough hair grew on top to support a new patch.

'Try me some, I don't wanna break a five.'

A surefire moocher is one who tells you he doesn't want to *break* a buck.

'Will you frame and worship it from your knees?'

Unable to hustle a bottle outside I turned toward the office. Chicago stood by my vehicle like he might do it harm. I vowed to myself that should he break glass or scratch paint I would return with dybuk, follow and block him in where it might be, pull him out and lay on until he begged for life and breath. So I loved my little vehicle more than anything until I

96

laid eyes on her. She had Cherokee blood. Most Louisville Negroes said they were part Cherokee but in her it was to see: red hue, wide nose, gilded cheekbones. She wore no powder or lipstick. Her hair looked chemicaled but bounced of its own. Her boyish fingers were without rings or polish and like all fast clerks behind a counter she was lean. I had not started my presentation when she swiped the bottle from my hand.

'HG9, Ancient Hair Grower! This works?'

'A man begins to lose, it fills an empty space.'

She was sold. 'I'll get a bottle for my uncle. How much?'

'$2.'

She searched a red wallet. 'I have five. I won't have enough for breakfast.'

It sounded odd. Granme could have made twenty breakfasts out of $5.

She was curious. 'This real? You didn't just fill it up?'

Two drivers watched nearby.

Pulling the cork she took a whiff. '*Woooh!*'

She gave it back. More drivers crowding us I thought to return when they were on the road. I drove to a firehouse I'd been asked back to, served coffee and a square of cornbread. Leaving with a sale I swung past Dixie Cab and a boyish figure in jeans walking roadside. On second glance I braked and backed up to her.

'Oh, you the one with the hair grower.'

'Where are you off to?'

'Gene's for breakfast.'

'You get time to go eat?'

'I'm off, I work eight to eight.'

'Oh, you work nights.'

'Now you got it.'

'Going to Gene's in your jeans?'

She did not laugh. She laughed only at crude, taxi drivers' jokes. Gentle wit left her cold. She swiveled into the red bucket seat.

'This is nice. You gonna get some breakfast?'

'I'll have a little something.'

Come to a diner ahead she quipped to some drivers just gotten off. Inside she waved to one and all, the gap between her teeth splitting her smile. She came here not just for breakfast but to socialize. Taking a table she seemed not to notice my limp. She ordered the 14-inch platter: three pancakes three eggs three hot links three slices of toast. I asked for tea. She and the waitress gave a look like tea alone was inappropriate in a hash house, 14-inch platter the norm. Though she just worked a 12-hour shift she made no more than $25 I guessed. Here she was ordering a $3 breakfast she could have fixed for 50 cents. At some tables I saw a dollar tip. Like she said, breakfast here took up most of $5.

'Tell me about the bottle,' she said, 'how many you sell a day.'

She could get to the point. How many I sold a day was what it was about.

'It's new. Once it makes a name for itself I see selling a box or two daily. I plan to have it all over Louisville, distributing from a central warehouse. It's small but will get bigger.'

Her platter came. 'I know all about sumthin' small gettin' bigger.

She worked on her breakfast, a bite of this a bite of that, not eating one thing at a time like I liked to. Pushing it all away she left some of everything. By the way she sagged when the waitress refilled her coffee it looked it would take her an hour to finish a second cup. I could have been downtown making a sale but was ready to forfeit the morn. The check was put in front of me, pre-arranged by eye signals between her and the waitress.

'Tell me about yourself,' she said taking my mind off the check. 'You been married?'

'No, you?'

'I had a boyfriend in Hopkinsville, sure felt like I was married, I couldn't get away.'

'Why?'

'He one those Negroes who don't just fade away, he come back to cut your tires. No less he took a psychology course and start comin' roun' diggin' in the desk drawers of my mind. I knew I had to get out of there then. Lettin' a crazy person take a psychology course, that should be agin' the law itself.'

'What's your schedule now?' I asked.

'Usually I sit awhile, then go piddle roun' my place 'til noon, sleep, pack a sandwich and banana, and head straight back to Dixie, six days a week, twelve hours a day, not five and eight like you regular people.'

'You don't get tired, all those hours?'

'You don't know me, I'd work Sunday they let me.'

'It's good to like work.'

'Nights depend on me. I get calls, get the address right and relay it loud and clear. Starts with me, goes from there.'

She took the words out of my mouth, how I would have done her job.

She perked up. 'You gonna take me home?'

I paid the check, my first extravagance, nearly $5 from my pocket for breakfast. I drove her to a structure built over a starter shop. Many roadside businesses in Louisville put a living structure overhead. We went up at the side. She opened the door on a long narrow room, refrigerator and table afore, bed, dresser and lamp beyond. She pulled out a chair for me.

'How long has the place below been closed?' I asked.

'He's not closed. He goes gets cars started, ten bucks a call plus labor and parts – parts he rebuilds hisself. Ten bucks for just goin', even if it's just downroad.'

'You can't get your car started, you're stuck,' I supposed.

'He ain't even a real mechanic. He goes that starter-alternator route. I had a car up from Hopkinsville nickel-dimin' me. Five bucks here, ten bucks there. Finally a guy wants a hundred for sumthin'. I told him keep it, I'll just walk.'

I looked around. Neat it was yet eery.

'You're alone here at night sleeping?'

'I sleep daytime. I told you I work six nights a week. You hear or are you *deaf?* I finish Saturday mornin' and take a bus to Hopkinsville, see my mother and brother, come back Sunday noon and get ready to go to work.'

'It would seem lonely here nights,' I suggested.

'It don't feel right daytime. Man down there one of those foreingers keep givin' me the eye. You know what they want. I put out a sign *Do not disturb* so customers don't come up and knock. They do it anyway.'

'You ought to move.'

'I got no time to look.'

Of my trailer I said naught.

'How long are you here now?'

'A year here a year at Dixie, come together, one down-road from the other.'

'You couldn't find work in Hopkinsville?'

'There's work with military. I could've got a job but I told you I had to get away from my boyfriend.'

'He doesn't come looking for you?'

'He don't know where I am. Even if he did he ain't nuthin' in Louisville. He think he quick in Hopkinsville, he ain't nuthin' but a hillbilly here. I know drivers who carry thirty-eights. They know laws of self-defense good as lawyers. They know when you can shoot. One of 'em shot a cop in Florida and got away with it. He has a scrapbook. You the type to shoot a cop, you the type to shoot anybody

100

anytime with no compunctions. He come up here menacin'
anybody, he better watch out. It was my own damn fault. I
knew who I was takin' up with. Granny used to say "Deal in
honey, girl, you got a little honey to lick; deal in gold, chile,
you got a little gold to wear; deal in shit, baby, you got shit!"
Does the simplicity of that come over?'

I savored her Granme's wisdom. 'Simplicity is the
essence of beauty.'

She pulled out her shirttail and reached for the sky.
Though she wasn't tall everything about her looked long. I
stiffened at her on her toes.

'You have Cherokee blood?' I breathed.

'That's what the family say, it just so happens at all get-
togethers I never seen one Indian – just shufflin' black folk
snatchin' all the chicken they can. How about you, you a
mulatto? You had a white daddy?'

'I'm mulatto but have no white parent. In Haiti
mulattoes almost always marry mulattoes. They take more
pride in white blood than Americans. In Haiti marrying a
Negro is considered a comedown.'

'Ain't that rotten apples? They Negro, lookin' down on
other Negroes.' She winked. 'I bet you think you better than a
darkie?'

'I'm not prejudiced. Sometimes I say nigger under my
breath but I won't let myself believe I'm better because my
skin is light.'

Her eyes shined. 'You a strange little guy the way you
talk and walk. Am I wrong . . . how would you describe
yourself?'

'I'm one who makes *his* business *his* business, getting
by nicely, thank you.'

'That's cute.'

From the refrigerator she took out a jug of wine. Articles
inside lined up by height, the jug was etched. I imagined

101

Granme putting it to use in her one extravagance – lighting candles.

She held it to her cheek. 'Muscatel?'

Not new to wine, my last year with Granme I oft took a cup ending Sunday song. She poured two juice glasses full. A sip of buttery warmth passed my lips, a treat it would be on cold eve of hardworked day.

'I go through a jug a week.' Clicking her glass on mine she scooped a little with pointed tongue. 'I don't get drunk – I just like to get drinky.'

She had a question. 'You speak so clearly. Is that your voice or do you talk like that for business purpose, like I do?'

'I try to speak clearly or why speak at all?'

She looked at me seriously. 'You went to college?'

'Two years at Louisville Downtown Extension. I was a schoolteacher for a short time.'

'You don't look like a teacher.'

'Samuel Clemmens during the strike.'

'Oh, they take just about anybody. We had one 80-year-old teacher in a strike. He walked and let farts at the same time.'

'You still need knowhow or the class turns into chaos.'

'I bet you were good all through school, didn't get in no trouble.'

'I didn't go through school. I got to seventh grade.'

'*How* you went to college you just got to seventh grade?'

'I educated myself. I delivered suits downtown from twelve years old and made time to read. I also did crosswords. Education rendered smartly builds like change in a jar.'

She took me in with drowsy eyes. 'I always thought that was a good job. Teachers in Hopkinsville never sweated nuthin', 'specially the men.'

'I liked teaching, I like doing business better. I like to come up with an idea to make money.'

'I get ideas all the time but don't know what to do with 'em.'

'I will help if you trust me.'

'I didn't you wouldn't be here.' She ran a finger around the table. 'You wanna *sit* or make time?'

Surely, I thought, she did not mean what it sounded like but she went to privy and came out in a red kimono barely over her buttocks. At a plume of red undergrowth between her legs, mine together took hold of my organ. She sat down at the foot of the bed and beckoned me. I went to her, my pants a size large as a fervent salesman's usually are.

'Well.'

Hard of breath I slipped off shirt and necktie. Pleased with my fine little chest she slid back and spread her knees, her undergrowth unhusked so to speak. Humming through my nose I pulled my pants up over my brace.

'What's on your leg?'

'I was kicked by a Tonton Macoute, when a small boy.'

I unbuckled the straps.

'What in hell is a Tonton Macoute?'

'Papa Doc Duvalier, you know of him? He had a private militia he turned loose on mulattoes. I was with Granme and mama in camp. Two old soldiers saw them coming and ran away in their drawers. As leader of the small ones I stepped forward and a Macoute kicked me three feet off the ground. After they took all they could I was taken to Port au Prince. A fake doctor set my leg bone so it grew in two places.'

Now I said what I long entertained. 'I heard his name, he who kicked me, *Jacobin*. I will go back one day.'

'You gonna kill him I bet?'

'To take revenge in Haiti you need only pay as you go. Authorities do not stand in the way of justice as they do here. I will find him. Take that down. I have not yet made an empty threat.'

103

'Who else you gonna kill? I hear once you start it's easy.'

Biding no more talk I unbuckled my belt. Granme always said underwear for a young man serves more oft embarrassment than utility – that well-wove trousers suffice for warmth and modesty. Letting them down my organ lept in her eyes.

'*Oh no, baby!* Pull them back up. It's too big.'

I looked down at what I always thought standard size.

'This is not a big one. In Haiti it is said all the big deeks are in Barbados.'

'Baby, you expect a skinny girl like me to take all that?'

I did not know what to say for myself.

'Come here,' she relented.

I came closer and she tried to get her mouth around me.

'I don't want that.' I stepped back.

'You don't want mouth love? What *man* don't want that?'

I sat down beside her, my organ standing of its own.

'I loved you as soon as I saw you.'

'How you love me soon as you saw me?'

'I am not one to tarry.'

On second thought she scooted back to a shelf, put ointment on a finger and swung her legs apart in my eyes revealing purplish openings, one tight as a buttonhole, the other looking worse for wear. Working her finger through its ruffles it was soon glutinous. From my knees I leaned across barely reaching her lips. She turned her face.

'Flick your *tongue!* You ain't doin' nuthin' pushin' on my mouth.'

Stung by her sharp words, I meant but innocent foreplay by rubbing up against her hipbone.

'You ain't had *none?* Get out yo' pants and get between my legs.'

Holding me back with one hand she took in but half from the other. *Hooo! Aaah! Aaah!* Buttocks aquiver I began to thrust. Unearthly light bathing my eyes I lost all bearing, my organ leaping on its own. Arching up I growled in relief and shook like a dog after a sneeze. She pushed out from under me, snatching up tissue, pushing it inside, leaving her fingers dripping.

'*Look* at this mess! This all been in you, you brought it down on me?'

Limping to privy she caught what she could under her and came out to wipe the floor.

'Do I look like Secretariat? Naw, baby, I didn't bargain for this. You need a woman who's had two or three babies and wear her hair up like a sex maniac.'

I lay back, jaws locked.

'I got hips like a boy. You think I can take all that? Why can't you be like other men? Every man like a woman to put it in her mouth.'

'I'm not like all men, I'm of royal blood. My blood goes back to Louis XVI of France.'

'Is that sumthin' you say, then somebody else say *that* and twenty cents gets you a cup of coffee at YMCA?'

'No, should France take back the throne they will come find me. I am the last of the royal blood.'

'Why wouldn't they just pick a handsome prince?'

'It would not do. Even enemies of a king will have no common counterfeit. To bow to a king he must be one.'

'Why you not important?'

'Because France threw over the throne two hundred years ago. Should they decide else they will go to the ends of the earth and break doors to find me.'

'Oh, baby, you innocent, you clean and polite, I hope you don't expect me to take all that more than once a week. And please don't ever come up on me from behind. I get tight as a drum when I bend over. You'd tear me a new one.'

She said that thinking of me as a boyfriend.

I was now on the go all day. After early hours at Take-A-Part touting HG9, I drove overhill and went building to building till early eve, then on to the donut shop, dialing my number for who had called, calling back and waiting over tea for a customer or two. Enterprise complete I combed my hair, stopped at a liquor store for a bottle of Coke a Cola and bag of peanuts, then drove to Dixie Cab to keep Charlene company as she nibbled and sipped, neat even in snacking. I sat tutoring her about all I had read, telling her names of countries she didn't know existed. She knew little of world climates. When I told her that at the tip of South America our winter is their summertime and vice versa, she would not believe January February March could be summer anywhere. I explained the revolution of Earth, climate the tilt we take to the sun.

Describing much of Earth to her I told her stories of great persons. Near nothing she knew of Harriet Tubman who from my reading shaped up to be the greatest American. Grinning as she nibbled, I never belabored a point believing royal blood won't hear to it from others or oneself.

Oft-times she cringed like I was making it up. I liked to emphasize by tapping her tomboy fingertips and leaning over to peck her lips, which she didn't mind, but at a call she perked up with pencil and pad to take info. At that moment I was not there to her. Ten o'clock or so I drove home with the top down listening to the old teenager music. Nights of heaven they were.

Fridays I picked her up at Dixie Cab to take her to Gene's for breakfast, putting down 50 cents tip. For the money I spent Granme bought beans spaghetti shankbones to feed us a week. She knew what I was doing she would try to crawl out of the ground. Most all ordered 14-inch platters because a patron's status at Gene's was in the breakfast ordered. Charlene nudged me to get a big breakfast but I insisted on tea and éclair. I did not want to bloat myself with

106

excess food I did not need or deserve before I did any work. Else she seemed pleased even though I was two inches shorter and swung a leg. Sitting down she took a bottle of HG9 from the box and put it out, talking it up to anyone come by.

Gene the owner stopped. 'This grow hair?'

Combed back over a spot, 45 or so he looked.

He studied the label. 'You been comin' roun', I been seein' you.'

He meant by it I should give him a bottle, a full head of hair that went with it, none of it, of course, to cost a dime. All come true he would not have been so good to pick up the check. I knew the Southern businessman well and he was usually a skunk behind his 'Howdy!'

He dallied, Charlene knocking my knee.

'How much a bottle?'

'Two dollars.'

'Two dollars! I can run a girl an hour for that.'

Getting no reply he went to the front and brought back $2. Usually I gave each sale a blessing it should work for the buyer; this time I didn't care.

Since that day, I worked for Jews Greeks Lebanese and other types known for business. They ranged from sports to screws but even the worst had a sense of doing a customer some good, but when it came to the Southern business owner, he would not give what was black under his nails could he help it, yet had the audacity to call good Negroes, *niggers*, when he was the nigger by definition in Webster's Dictionary.

She was in such spirit Friday morns, conversationing in all her glory, munching toast and hot links at my side, oft reaching under the table to fondle me a ready listener to anything she had to say. She would get up to stretch twitching her buttocks, swiveling in red loafers. I could not take my eyes off her.

Making $25 a day six days a week she had trouble paying $50 a month rent. She told me she took money to

Hopkinsville. She dropped hints – rent is coming –telling me her landlord, a foreigner of heavy accent called *bohemians* by black people in Louisville, came up to snoop, asking if she wanted wine. It made me angry – a foreigner thinking a Negro girl would give sex if he offered cheap wine.

I determined she should move in. Driving to a storage lot I rented five foot by five $5 a month. I moved raw product bottles labels there.

She came on a Sunday with a box holding a second pair of jeans, flannel shirts, underthings, a lavender dress and red blanket. She brought no cosmetics, not even skin soap, strictly opposite of glamour girls whose need for artificial beauty was sad to me. I welcomed her with half a cake. She was now twice as far from work. Above the starter shop she was a mile down Independence Road, walking unless a Dixie Cab pulled over. Now she had to hop on a bus.

Else Sunday and Friday morn we still only saw each other at Dixie Cab. When I left the trailer at daybreak she was still on the job. She took up so little room it seemed hardly different there until I got back one eve and saw a telephone, let down she didn't ask permission, yet asking myself what sort of man was I to have no telephone there in case of an emergency – but I lied to myself? What emergency could befall a young couple without child? Odds were against it. A comer like me couldn't cover all the bases. Cutting corners on good odds could make all the difference.

Three weeks on I found a bill for $15 on the table. I looked it over. Not one number she called in Hopkinsville but three. She never asked me to come along. She said she didn't because her family would hand me hard luck stories about medical problems they needed money for, then want me to take them to A&W for burgers and floats. She needed say no more. That deterred me from *ever* wanting to meet those people.

She left the bill just like on our first day she had the waitress at Gene's put it in front of me. I took it to the telephone company and paid. I didn't want to see it loiter.

She was costing me $35 a month in breakfasts and telephone but if you are not a pimp – low of the low next to a pawnbroker – a woman costs money. It is life.

Alas HG9 didn't take hold the way I expected it to. Goldenrod fuzz neither grew thicker nor higher. Without further applications it waned. I sensed an ingredient Granme added I couldn't recall, remembering only old soldiers' urine she retrieved and added vinegar to. Nothing else came to mind other than her boiling up large glossy leaves. Possibly the milky skim of those leaves yielded the enzyme missing in my potion. I couldn't recall any other way she used them. I'd had years to get a complete formula out of her, one missing ingredient to grow hair, to have a substance worth a rajah's palace. But Granme was at fault as much as I. A secret of such value she did not care to pass on. Oft I wondered if in her silent nature she was not touched. This inclusion – was there one – could have made all the difference.

Charlene was laid off Sunday nights. She couldn't wait to go back to work after returning from Hopkinsville Sunday noon. Now Dixie Cab determined not to take Sunday calls but let cabs pick up downtown-to-Fort Knox fares, unobliged to run to private calls, many of which on Sunday nights were made by cranks. I would have a night to sleep with her. We had not yet slept together. She slept bare. I savored how warm she would be of curve and hollow when we awoke Monday morn.

Instead of what I expected those eves, they nearly broke me. Sunday I cut short at Take-*A*-Part to go to good ground to stand over Granme, then started home 3 o'clock or so, my stomach in knots. By then Charlene drank most of the muscatel she bought Saturday morn. I would bring home a roasted chicken and cut off wings and legs for her but she looked at them funny. All drunks look at food funny. It wasn't breakfast meat: sausage links patties, it wasn't good eating as far as she was concerned. She resented not going to work, taking it out on me. Any topic brought up turned against me, I offered to take her to the Coronet but she was a conversationalist and thought movies a big nothing.

I reasoned: why can't she be good? Was it tragic losing a night of work, a sixth of her pay? She had a roof, paid no rent, but by 8 o'clock my every gesture was repaid by looks of wanting to lunge at me. I sat winding my thumbs. In bed any attempt to slide a finger from behind was met with a loud NO!

'Where's this company you have? How come you never take me there? What's the address?'

'I told you it's a little warehouse to mix and bottle raw material.'

'You said you had a company. I thought you had machines and belts.'

'It's not far off. I'm selling half a box some days.'

'You really had a company you'd show me. Between us I think you like to give impressions you're sumthin' you're not.'

'Why talk like this? Granme mama I lived without complaint. You know the saying two can live as one. With us it was three; it could have been four. We lived peacefully. Why must you want to quarrel Sundays?'

By now I was being openly ridiculed at Gene's and she was enjoying it. Behind my back, drivers mocked me to her heart's content. When we arrived, a driver with bushy white hair, called 'Professor' and 'Einstein', lurched to the counter swinging a leg behind him to which she put a hand over her mouth.

Children can be cruel in mimicry but no schoolmate ever mimicked my limp. Some admired me for keeping up. But these taxi drivers made me their private joke at Gene's for my crooked leg and the éclair and cup of tea I ordered. I did a

110

slow burn as they pretended to sip from one hand and nibble from the other.

I had a catch sewn into the lining of my jacket to conceal dybuk on my person because I sensed these jibes would grow violent. These drivers would not be satisfied until they did me harm. Directing dybuk like a fly-whisk, snapping it to and fro in Charlene's eyes I told her many a punk had had a taste. I thought to confront *Einstein* in the restroom, lay him out with one blow, and as he cringed under urinals speak from the edge of my teeth,'You still want to make fun of how I walk, Professor Einstein, do you?'

I knew not what she saw in these white men, that whatever they said made her laugh while she hardly listened to me. One afternoon I sat at the donut shop bethought. Even young I knew I would be able to stand on my own two feet, that pluck would get me by, yet not even the back of my mind held I would one day take a wife. Even with my baby face and curls in school no girls made eyes at me. They wanted a whole boy even then. When I left school and went downtown no female I passed on the street in five years gave a second look.

Could I think else than I'd grow old alone? But if I married Charlene I could always say I once had a wife with red skin and hair, her underthings neatly folded in our little bureau. I could prove by marriage certificate she once belonged to me. Too, where would I find another who wore neither powder nor polish, shunned mirrors, wanted watched no television and never asked to adorn herself? Would it last only a year I would not wind up an old limper who had never had a woman. It would provide succor in lonely hours.

I went to the bank, took the last money out of my account. A Jewish jeweler to whom I had delivered suits said to come to him once I found a girl. Knowing nothing I went. He showed me a diamond on a gold band so slight it looked a child's. I asked something bigger for the price and he showed a red ruby on silver, the best I could get he said. Trustful, I remembered Mel recommending him and Mel not a type to recommend a dishonest man. He put the ring in a snap box, asking if I wanted it wrapped. The box would do.

I sold eight bottles, a good sign on the day I was going to propose. A gusty night she was in one of her better moods at work. I could see it in the way she nibbled peanuts in the gap of her teeth and sipped from the bottle. As usual I watched her every move.

'Charlene, I would marry you.'

'Why would you marry me, Daupin?'

'I'll never find anyone like you. I think of you almost every moment. If this arguing will only stop I'll be —'

The velvet box snapped open she pinched the ring between thumb forefinger. I let her put it on herself.

'I want to look at you and know you're mine. Will you marry me?'

She kept a straight face best she could.

Left at that I let it build in her head. Friday morn I picked her up at Dixie Cab as usual, then passed Gene's on our way downtown where we showed identification at City Hall and applied for a license, fee $30 wait 30 days while our backgrounds were checked for undisolved marriages and fugitive status.

They did not pass lightly. I asked her to keep our engagement secret but soon all of Dixie Cab and everyone at Gene's knew about the ruby on her finger. Just one waitress she told she said – I told her that was equal to telling half of Louisville with nary an exception. I suspected those filthy drivers made sport of me to her and the help at Gene's told her she could do better, but she said nothing of it. Each day by, so far so good I counted until a glint came into her eyes and her eyes did not shine in goodness. I feared she was bringing me along to the last day to make a joke of it in front of her friends.

It came, September 8. She'd didn't bring it up on the eve, nor did I. Lightly slept I sped to Dixie thinking now in front of the changeover she would reject me, giving all the drivers the laugh they craved. She got into the pony like any other Friday and we returned to the gully. She made me wait outside while she changed, thinking I would attempt a quick coupling seeing her bare at that early hour.

She came out in girlish lavender cut too high in the sleeves for her round tomboy shoulders. Driving to City Hall with the top down we rose to third floor stepping up in line to sign our certificate. I coaxed her into trading vows crosshanded cheek to cheek in the old Hatian colonialist way. The ruby slipped back on her finger we were pronounced man and wife by a threadbare preacher I gave five dollars to. Hand in hand we skipped off. Turnbow in uniform happened to be there. Holding the elevator, his eyes went agape, '*Dammmmm!*' carried to the end of the corridor. Pushing in with us his jaw hung open until Charlene said, 'Why don't you close *yo'* mouth!' Grinning like children we skipped through lobby and down the walk.

I nearly forgot those Sunday eves she belittled me. Going about with spring in my step, spurned as usual at barber shops, I stopped at downtown beauty parlors where the operators were receptive. In no time a Jewish charmer pawed me to tell her why HG9 was growing hair on her customers, wanting to know what I'd mixed up that was so virile. It worked better on women and I was reinvigorated to its value.

Each day I followed Ridge Road farther, stopping at parlors, using a proprietress behind as a reference. I went this sub-route right after my two hours at Take-*A*-Part then got to downtown at 11 which was about the time most offices would suffer a salesman.

Just as it seemed HG9 was turning the corner, Dixie Cab determined to not take calls weekends but let drivers freelance. Charlene's pay fell to $100 a week. She had no rent to pay I reminded her, but when I got back to the gully Friday eve she was with jug ready to tear into me. Then my roadster had its first problem. Two brothers at 4th St. Garage told me to pick it up Saturday. Taking the bus all week, returning Friday eve I coaxed conversation from a young nurse. Sensing she was down I inquired about her work. She was ready to give up because she strained her back lifting patients. I asked if she got no help. She said orderlies weren't around when needed and half her graduation class had stopped working. She told of patients that are dead weight, slipping through their arms. She spoke of obstinate oldsters hard as all get-out to move. Listening I kept an eye out on black idlers in front of liquor stores, the sight of them on every corner melding with her lament.

Coming in on Charlene I could tell how much she drank by how much of the phone charm was out of her voice. By the way she sat it was hard to say. I put the peanuts and Coke a Cola down. Everything in the trailer was neat as a pin.

'I have an idea.'

'What?'

'On the bus a young nurse said half the girls she graduated with are out of work because of bad backs and ruptures.'

'*Ruptures!* How women get ruptures?'

'A tear by the intestines, it can happen to anyone.'

'I thought you had to be like the Chinaman with one hung low.'

'What a waste, a graduation class half out of commission.'

'What do nurses do so all dang hard to be out commission?'

'Patients are miserable and fight. Try to move them they're dead weight. Nurses rip their backs and sides.'

'So?'

114

'Listening I kept one eye out at young black men standing on corners. What if a hospital has one on every floor so these girls won't ruin their backs?'

'I seen black guys in hospitals all the goldang time.'

'Mopping floors and cleaning toilets. This job is *gallant*, prestige in uniform, not hospital wear. I have a name, *Groneg* – Creole for brutes who do heavy lifting. I see them using their brawn to keep the peace. When relatives come yelling their heads off, first they will face them, so nurses save their backs and feel safe. These *Gronegs* are heroes in their eyes at what cost – a mere $3 an hour on every floor.'

'I bet that's where you come in. You gon' be chief bottlewasher and all these black bucks gon' bring you some of their pay.'

'I take no one's pay. Hospitals will pay us a small premium for every shift a *groneg* works. We could open an office and start registration. I will go to hospitals with the proposal. And with your phone ability you will make sure a *Groneg* is available for every shift so when one is needed he should not come from another floor.'

A long Louisville Indian Summer turned cold and she didn't like the cold. Asking me when we would get started I asked patience, needing to get HG9 selling at a box a day.

It took two weeks for her to lose it. 'You'll never gonna get to this. It's just hot air. Wutch you waitin' for? You gon' do sumthin' – do it.'

I could have written up a proposal, had it typed and gone to hospitals with it. There was even a local government office to help responsible black men develop business ideas. We could have rented desk space downtown and with just one hospital signed up kept going. HG9 was only partially effective, something missing in its makeup. I only kept thinking the lost ingredient was in back of my head and would come to mind.

One strangely peaceful Sunday eve as we played checkers she cocked her head and for no reason I could see said 'Sometimes, I feel like killin' myself – *first* I'm gonna kill you.' I didn't know to take it as whimsy or intent? Sitting with her Monday at Dixie Cab she let slip drivers gave her rides after breakfast at Gene's. Tuesday morn after selling three bottles at Take-*A*-Part I doubled back to a cab parked at the stoop. Cold out I took it Charlene might invite a co-worker in. Wednesday there was a different numbered cab there, seeming to me drivers took turns giving her lifts. Thursday there were two with one driver outside enjoying a smoke.

She quit going to Hopkinsville and now had all weekend to get at me. First Sunday in December I went to Take-*A*-Part and stayed all day selling four bottles. I did not go to good ground as usual, stopping to watch a fire near the liquor store where I picked up a Coke a Cola and peanuts for Charlene.

She was waiting, the muscatel all gone.

'How come you late? You always get here early.'

'A building burned down on Morgan.'

'And you one them like to stand there and watch? Too bad you didn't burn with it. I need a ride to Roy's.'

'For what?'

'More wine, that's what.'

'You drank enough.'

'I had three glasses.'

'The bottle was half full when I left, you had your fill.'

'Had my *fill?* I'm gon' sit here and look at your face? You think you gon' put that thing of yours up in me? *Hell no! Hell damn no!* You gon' give me a ride or you gon' get nuthin'.'

I put down the peanuts and Coke a Cola. 'This must stop, I beg you. I will get sick. When Granme was here there was not one angry word.'

'I heard that one goddam time too many. How long you gon' tell me 'bout your granny? How come you never say nuthin' 'bout your mama? Yo' mama didn't talk? Yo' mama retarded? What you come from, a retarded girl? Yo' ol' granny bent her over and let some tramp bone her so she could have a little houseboy runnin' chores?'

She went to privy without closing door. Else a sharp rectal sizzle there was blessed silence.

She came straight to. 'You sleep with yo' granny? I see one bed here. You sleep with yo' granny, get some that old stuff?'

Warning her off with my hand, she cupped hers like a man at a urinal, bowlegging closer.

'Spread your legs, granny. This gonna fill you up 'til Christmas.' She curled her lips over her teeth. 'Give it to yo' ol' granny, sonny. Wutch you think I keep you 'roun for, anyway?'

Backward I stepped.

'Have back I say!'

'You ain' gon' do nuthin', little itty bitty shit.'

I swung dybuk out from under my coat.

'Oh, you gon' show me that? You not a full-size man so you gon' scare me. Do it then, little itty bitty shit, do it!'

She charged and I smote hip and buttock.

'*Ahooooooooo!*'

Dropped on her tailbone she retreated on both heels to a corner.

'I'll call the cops! I'll call the goddam police on you, you sonovubitch!'

At her crazed shriek I buttoned up. A second shriek followed me out, making my head ring. Left groggy by what I'd done I limped a good while in snowfall before turning back around and returning to a police car in the gully. Going wide I ducked behind rough thicket across the road. Two police were on the stoop. Else red blanket over her shoulders

117

she was bare at the door pointing where I laid into her. Flashlights running up her hip, veered oft to loin and buttock. Giving them their fill she told them to go find me.

'He roun' here, his car still here.'

'Not now,' said one. 'You want to bed down at YWCA?'

'He ain't far, he just a little bitty shit with a short leg. He carry a petrified horse dick to whip up on anybody who get in his way. He got one of them complexes he gon' show you what he can do.'

They flashed around in the darkness.

'Least take his car, make him come get it?'

'It's on private property.'

She came out with her things. A blanket that could have gone around her twice she trailed like a cape to further expose herself. I could not understand this business of flaunting herself to white men. They put her in the police car and tore away.

Crossing over I sat awhile in the dark fearing they might return. Putting on a second pair of socks I took Granme's quilt and drove south on Freeman Road to a dirt lane, bundling up behind the wheel.

Shivering all night, oft out to urinate and shake feeling into my game leg, I knew I would walk stiff that day. Daybreak I turned back to wash up, determined that if she returned of different mind after a night at YWCA I would take her back. If not I had HG9 and trusted pony to go forth.

Arrived at Take-*A*-Part I warmed myself with coffee then proceeded to sell three bottles. Driving the sub-route down Ridge Road to beauty shops I sold four. Circling back past strikers out front of Western Casing I pulled over a block ahead as was my wont to come up on a place collecting my thoughts. Intruding on four men in conversation, the bottle was grabbed from my hands.

'My brother-in-law at the bus yard used this.'

He pulled the cork for a whiff. 'This is the shit. Make it two, I'll get one for him.'

His excitement brought more strikers. In minutes I sold all twelve in the box. A good few told me come morrow with more. Off I went of mind to suffer Charlene no more. What sort of individual I asked myself hates who loves her? I doubted this could be corrected for she was one to either sit at your feet or go for your throat, a derangement that I believe is congenital and won't be middled.

Come upon a police car at the stoop I pulled off ahead and went back afoot. Assuming they brought her back I crouched in thicket wondering what was taking so long in there. Out came Charlene and Turnbow grinning insipidly like two first getting to know one another. Getting in the car he tore out leaving ruts.

Slipping inside I gave her a start.

'What was that policeman doing here? That's Turnbow, the one at City Hall when we got married.'

'He drove me. He says I get hit again he's comin' back and this time he's gonna make it personal.'

'What's that musky smell? What were you doing here so long?'

'Conversationing.'

'About who – *me?*'

'He says he's had his eyes on you. He wants to know why you always carryin' that box downtown.'

'No business his what I carry downtown, I know about him, too. White men started shooting at the 880 Motel and he crawled under a truck. That's who's going to protect you from me. Did you give him mouth sex here? You think I don't know what goes on when drivers take you back after your all-important breakfasts? Those white men don't do it free. They do nothing free. They wouldn't give you rides, you didn't hold their things in your mouth in the sanctity of our little home. Smelly white men who sit in a cab all day, why because they work for Dixie Cab?'

She answered in a way that convinced me she was brainwashed. 'They hired guns who go out in public service and take guff off nobody and no one. Louisville wouldn't survive if Dixie Cab wasn't flowing through its arteries. It would cramp up.'

'Why would a city halt because stinking cab drivers aren't out on the road? They probably came to Louisville because they couldn't make it anywhere else. The one called professor, why isn't he professoring? Why is he driving people?'

'Better than beggin' door to door to buy that crap of yours.'

'I beg nobody. Nobody has to give me a cab to go drive fares. In parts of the world people don't hand them money, they throw it on the ground.'

'They're businessmen. They rent a piece of equipment and go make money with it.'

'A *real* businessman needs only his mind. Whatever is available, whatever's unwanted undesirable, he thinks of a way to move it. I collect raw urine from an old Jewish tailor and move that and it doesn't cost me a dime. That's using your head! *That's* doing business!'

'You runnin' pee in those bottles? People usin' pee on their heads?'

'It works, that's all it has to. I just sold twelve bottles to strikers at Western Casing. They grabbed them up and begged me to come back. I'll take a full box there morrow morn and make $50 while those stinking Dixie drivers are at Gene's sitting over coffee. HG9 will start selling itself and I'll move on. You don't want to come with me you can stay behind.'

I drove to storage and poured all raw product I had, bottling forty, this forty sure to be special. There were a hundred strikers out on the plaza at Western casing, many

120

thinning under their hats. Word of mouth through Louisville would launch HG9. It would not take long once it started.

Downtown I had no more than stepped into a hotel beauty parlor when Louise told me she wanted ten bottles. I wanted to ask if it had done wonders on somebody's head but she was all business as usual, handing me a twenty, the first I received in a transaction. I put it in my wallet and drove to the bus yard. Going full circle I sold a bottle. I did not ask the buyer if he was the one who recommended HG9 to the striker. When business is good, better less asked and said.

Five bottles left in the box I went to my old standbys, Downtown Reality and the optical company below, selling three. Calling the answering service I was told two customers were stopping by the donut shop. I sat over tea and both showed. Never had I such a day.

I didn't pick up the usual bag of peanuts and Coke a Cola for Charlene but drove to the gully thinking of a way to save our marriage. I determined to borrow money and open the *Groneg* office, putting her in charge, soonby seeing in her eyes the foolishness of misplaced loyalty to Dixie Cab. She would gladly work the phone seven days – all the better.

Snow began to fall like for Christmas. Inside the trailer I had a full box of HG9 ready for the morn. Like I'd told Charlene it hardly cost a dime, sleeping on that.

Ridge Road was packed down, vehicles spun off and abandoned. Slowly I went up over the hill to Western Casing and parked off road. Food service trucks pulled up, civilities of the first day done with, strikers around barrels flaming two feet high yelled that on a day like this at least coffee should be free. I walked up to 'Here he comes!'

Three customers I took in minutes, three more came wanting to hear what HG9 could do. Beginning with a proviso that had they not lost too much from the crowns of their heads I told them HG9 would grow back soft thin patch. They were going into their pockets when a police car turned to the curb

121

and the driver window came down. In leather jacket gloves earmuffs Turnbow sounded his bullhorn.

'Ya'll rubbin' Jew piss on yo' heads? He sellin' old Jew piss in those bottles.'

'What's in here?' asked a striker.

'Natural carbon nitrogen product,' I breathed. He pulled the cork for a whiff. 'This *piss* in here? We're on strike and you sellin' piss to use on our heads?'

A hand gripped my shoulder – I did not look round for it was gentle – followed by a whack on the head from the other. Letting go of the box I was grabbed by the collar in attempt to roll me. Here rough playground experience and agility to pounce off pavement paid off. Slammed down I came back up like a target in a gallery. Three strikers around me, five six more closing in, a steel-toed boot split my buttocks. Half pointing the way I tried to leapfrog a flaming barrel. Flames leaping in response (*Yaaaaagh!*) I kicked it over, stumbling through ash and fire until with a last leap I knocked over the sawhorse at the curb. To the bullhorn's *'Break his neck! Break his goddam neck!'* my leg jumps were like those of a jackrabbit. A Volkswagon veering round the plaza spun its wheels. Climbing it from behind I slid back, catching hold of bumper and riding free. Twisting over downhill, my heels danced in fright. I let go careening through a snow bank and down under trees, stumbling back twice before gaining my feet. Feeling about making sure I was whole, I was saved but my pony would surely be wrecked in revenge by those who saw me arrive.

Climbing over snowbank I trudged downhill, looking over my shoulder because a striker would not hesitate to run me down from behind. To flat ground I came to a laundry where I put my duster and socks in a dryer, sorry now I had taken up with Charlene in the first place. Sitting down to wait out the day I beared up to what I expected to see.

Midnoon taking more snow, I doubted strikers would stick it out. Striking back not the way I came but circling around, I came to Ridge Road at a place halfway between downtown and Western Casing. Trudging uphill I looked down over empty plaza below. My pony stood back alone. Running downhill I slid a ways and got up trembling at what stood before me: all four tires up, windshield and windows intact. By some rare mercy it was not assaulted. Getting in, the engine hummed to me like a living thing with a heart.

Stealing up on the trailer I don't know what I might have done come upon her. Taking pen and paper I wrote:

Charlene,

Merely I ask why? I took you in and for my goodness you made our humble domicile your bordello. Do you ever remind yourself of the red ruby on your wedding finger and the vows we made cheek to cheek? You will likely not see me again but you will always remain in my heart.

Forgive me for having loved you,
Daupin

Belongings thrown in the pony, that of immediate use in a pillowcase, I went back for Granme's quilt, alas too late to go to good ground and say good-bye. I had no notion when I might ever be back.

Eve milder than it had been awhile, I headed north. New place new luck goes an old Creole byword. I had heard of

123

Indianapolis as easy to get to know but not easy for a Negro to get a start in and Chicago the opposite.

I crossed the bridge to Indiana, not getting far in sudden snowfall. Tailing a truck to a 24-hour diner I slid into the lot and sat awhile at the counter. The manager told me of a motor court ahead. I would sit night through before spending $5 for a bed. Coming by again he said there was a leather bench by the restroom I could lie down on. Covered with my duster I slept warm, washing up before daybreak, going out to my cold little pony and wiping it of snow.

Following trucks till noon I got clear, pulling off once for fuel. Come to Illinois early eve, to titanic Chicago, I turned off short of the downtown buildings into skid row, flophouses five six stories high. Bums walked confidently with packages as though there was good commerce there. I had read that in population old bums come together in protection from young bums. I could find them in one building and get all the raw product I would ever need.

Come to a corner where street Negroes stood around more idle than the bums my pony with a Kentucky license plate caught looks. Eyeing me as easy prey two horsefaces in long leather coats came over a snow bank. Knowing the look I slid around making back for the freeway heading south. Exiting to a street with Christmas decoration overhead I turned a corner for no reason coming to a busy newsstand aside a pool hall.

Pulling over I stepped around the corner and looked through the plate glass window of a busy canteen with a billiards hall behind it. Inside I asked if there was a cheap sleep nearby and was pointed down Cermak Road. In walking distance, I left my pony and went to an old hotel, shown a room with a rail bed and fringed cover that gave off a stale odor when I sat down.

Paying $7.65 I took key and walked back to the pool hall thinking I would be cozier there until time to sleep. A hot dog stand caught my attention. Used to coarse fare, frankfurters at Unity picnics tasted like mush to me, mustard put on the flavor. Here for 65 cents I got a steamed red hot with crisp relish and diced tomatoes, all in warm bun with seeds. Biting into it I had never savored such wholesome goodness. I promised myself one every day I worked, the first habit of a few I developed in Chicago.

The canteen full of old Greeks and Slavs, called DPs there, I went to the back to watch the play at the pool tables. Spectator chairs bolted down on a ledge two-foot high, I took it all in, picking up on talk of merchandise being moved, from tires to leather coats to stereos –a den of thieves it was.

What use of skid row – I had neither bottles nor place to mix and pour product – I needed for now to draw daily pay? The pool hall closing at twelve I pulled up behind the hotel. I'd had the sense not to leave Granme's quilt behind or would have spent a night under old fringed cover, scratching for reason or not.

Daybreak I washed in the tub and returned to the pool hall for coffee and a sweet roll, another habit I would pick up. Waiting until eight I walked down Cermak Road, finding work in a record shop. The owner, a Jewish cripple, a seller-collector, was continually answering the phone. He seemed to know every record and label ever printed.

No real fixtures, not even a counter, but rows of troughs he wheeled along to select titles. Boxes stacked in back, the job was to bring them out and file LPs. He gave me a quiz in alphabetization – odd combinations of vowels and consonants I arranged in order and was put to work.

Starting before nine, finishing at six I went to get the red hot in steamed roll I'd promised myself. Sitting in the canteen content from a day's work and $24 pay I reminded myself I need spend a third at the hotel. Using my ears I picked up on Emil's buck-a-night bunks, asking DPs if it was near. Pointed one block down two over I came to a corner brownstone of the same build as all the others, one story in front with an upper deck at the rear.

A strapping bohemian (Southern definition) looked me up down. I said I had just taken a job and needed a bed to sleep. He saw I was part Negro but looked like one who trusted no one – white or other – which works to a Negro's benefit. I looked clean and he took me to the upper deck where bunks with bare springs stood in barrack, each covered by thin mattress, pillow and military blanket. Neat and warm there as good a dollar as a man could spend – 'a good Chicago thing' as DPs said.

Earliest to be there eve and out by eight morn I could bring neither food nor drink. I wanted to pay a week but he refused, saying it's a dollar as you go and paying ahead led to trouble. I went out to get Granme's quilt. I could have gone back to the pool hall for a few hours but was beat.

More bunkers came up until all were taken. I identified only one a worker like myself, a silent Mexican who worked twelve hours a day in a laundry, living on a few dollars and sending money home. Others were neighborhood loafers and bicycle riders. The last one up sounded educated, the only one to come over and introduce himself. Called Irv, he offered me the newspaper before consorting with the others. They told him what they had seen and done that day and he chose to comment on it or not, toying with them. I wondered what such a tall commanding individual was doing in this well-ordered flophouse.

He held out a hand for the paper.

'This a kick or what – dollar a night? Where'd you hear about it?'

'The pool hall on Cermak.'

'Lucked out, Ace. Emil doesn't let everybody in. One complaint – that's it, he won't let you back.'

'He runs a business. I respect a man who runs a business.'

126

'Hardboiled honky comes to Chicago and gets on a Cermak streetcar with three cents. Fare's five and the Irish bullhead throws him off. He's gone by that since. Come two cents short he won't let you by. It shows you don't have enough character to secure a night's sleep.'

'You have seen that?'

He didn't answer. 'You came at the right time, alright. Christmas he bakes a peach cobbler and brings it up.' He rolled his tongue in a lascivious way. 'Let me tell ya, the old way, lard crust and everything.'

'Sounds like you come every night?'

'I have five rental properties. A tenant goes or I evict I stay on the premises. Why spend even a buck if I can sleep free?'

'How does one come by five properties – if I may be nosy?'

He gave a look but answered. 'Neighborhoods change for the worse. Old people try to stick it out, then wind up selling for whatever they can get. I put a thousand down and pay mortgage from rent.'

'You don't mind my asking, what rent do you get?'

'You ask a lot. I average a hundred twenty per property.'

'You take $600 a month?'

'I bootleg two garages for sleepers, $75 each. Seven fifty comes in.'

'All you need do is collect?'

'Not so fast, Rockerfeller, my tenants are pigs. I get two, three calls a week about leaks, breaks they cause themselves.'

'You go fix them?'

'I fix nothing, incidental repairs their responsibility, lease front center. They scream like animals. *Not* my problem, pal. I start giving in on repairs they'll call every goddam day. They can bite the walls before I put myself out. Withhold rent I evict. Takes six weeks to get them out. One broke the walls looking for copper underneath – and those animals want me to do repairs? Landlords who give in screw themselves. I'll screw anybody before I screw myself. I like to be good to myself. Most of all I like to beat the system.'

'Beat the system?'

'I worked twenty-five years as an accountant subjecting myself to daily mental abuse until I saw a system out there, and if you can beat it you have joy on earth. You like movies?'

'Never saw one.'

'Why?'

'Never got around to it.'

'I see everything coming out. You think I pay $4 they want now for a ticket? I go in with a popcorn tub, say I'm a doctor and stepped out to make a call. I get waved right in, get a refill and see a new release. And not in these dumps around here, I go downtown to the best.'

Taken with my duster he folded it at the foot of the bunk.

'What's *this?* You carry a sap?'

He pulled out dybuk. 'You hold it like this and let a guy have it?'

'Correct.'

He seemed to doubt me so I stood up, whirled it overhead, snapped it to, then hooked it around from both sides. A villain ahead would have been cracked on the nose and lashed on both ears. He was amused.

'You've let guys have it?'

'I shun violence but *some* individuals – it's all they understand. I am like you. I like opportunity but there are those who will stand in your way for no good reason.'

Again I lashed around.

'Easy,' he said. 'Emil will be up. He doesn't like strange noises.'

We spoke next eve. He said to save up a thousand and he would find an income house for me and I could pay

128

mortgage from rent with some left over. The third night he came with a tape recorder playing a message that ran a good ninety seconds. I had never imagined such vile threats.

'Who is that?'

'A black guy with a white wife and two mixed bastards. I knew he was trouble. C'mon, we're going to collect rent.'

'He sounds ready to kill someone. You should call police.'

'Take your sap, give him a few; he'll change his mind.'

I took a step and stopped. 'I don't think I should mix in this.'

'Why?'

'I like to mind my own business.'

'After *all* I let you in on?'

He didn't show up awhile. A plumber named Stanley came with a small dog. He did work for Emil on the condition he could bring the dog up. Looking over I wondered why a handsome guy of trade would come sleep here for a buck a night.

The dog liked to dance. While he had a time with me, Stanley smoked on the side of the bunk with a buttcan between his feet, talking only when talked to. When he didn't come in next eve bunkers went on about him. He was married with two children and getting by when his wife took a secretarial job at a local college. One noontime he came home and caught her in bed with a black security guard at the school. It broke him. At the child support hearing the judge, a black man, was sympathetic to his condition and awarded the wife only $100 a month, despite her lawyer clamoring for three times that.

They said he was a master plumber but lived day to day. I thought I knew the problem without asking. He was a 'whatever you say' individual. Women got him inside and after repairs they sat him for coffee and talked an ear off. Asked how much, he charged only what he needed to get by.

Returning next eve he said he'd been on a job in LaGrange, handing a business card to a bunker to pass on. Shortly he was smoking. I sat down facing him.

'Did you say LaGrange?'

'You know somebody in LaGrange?'

The dog nosing around, I didn't answer.

'How long does it take you to get there?'

'An hour if it's moving.'

'Would you rather work closeby?'

'I work where it is.'

'Give me your business card, I can get you work around here.'

'You know people?'

'I knocked on doors. I like it, most people don't.'

He checked his shirt pocket. 'How many?'

'Twenty if you got them.'

'The box is in the truck.'

I woke before light as usual, waiting for him to smoke, toilet and come out to the truck. Finding a box of cards he pinched out a quarter inch.

'May I say you charge half what a call plumber does?'

He nodded.

'Would I be off to say you don't take a big mark-up on parts?'

'Enough to pay for gas and time.

'That's all I need to know for now.'

Waiting until eight before starting down the block, my knocks on two doors were unanswered. A woman stuck her head out the third.

I presented a card. 'I make appointments for a plumber, Stanley. He will look at a problem if you have one.'

'He knows what he's doing?'

'He's a master plumber.'

'Last guy I let in didn't know anything. He looked good 'cause he had lots of tools.'

'Whatever you have Stanley will fix it for half price.'
'Why half?'
'He has no overhead.'
She took me to a running toilet.
'I'll have him here first thing morrow.'
'He can't come today? It's on my nerves.'
'He's in LaGrange.'
I took down her name, Mrs. Skolsky, street number and problem.

If there was a run leak stop I was let in. Midnoon I had four appointments. I could have gone on but didn't know Stanley's pace.

He pulled up at seven, letting out the dog. Putting away in back he did not afford me a look.
'I have four appointments.'
'Where?'
'You'll hardly move your truck.'
'What kind of work?'
'Toilets sinks drains.'
'What's your slice? You ain't doin' it free.'
'Twenty percent of what you make. You make $100, give me twenty. I'll be there to help, whatever I can do.'
'I have a referral in LaGrange.'
'Can you put it off? I said you'd be early.'
He leaned against the truck with a cigarette.
'You do the work, I'll keep the customer out of your hair.'

Morn after he'd had a smoke, we went three doors down with a box and pole. Mrs. Skolsky's eyes widened at Stanley's handsome face and wavy hair. She took us to the toilet. Lifting the tank lid he checked the flush assembly and shut off water. Mrs. Skolsky looking on he drained the tank, unhooked tube and chain and fit a new rubber valve into the seat at bottom. Turned on, water rose up gently. Upstairs to a

131

leaking faucet he took apart the assembly and replaced the rubber washers and spring, the drip no more.

'How much?'

'Twenty.'

She paid asking for another card. We went two doors down to an elderly man who took us downstairs to a stopped basin and sewer. Underneath the tub Stanley undid the curve trap between drain pipes, stabbed out sediment, worked a steel brush through from both ends and screwed it back on. Water swirled down the drain. Sopping up a puddle over the sewer grill he managed to unscrew it and worked the pole down while I poured in two bucket's full. The old fellow gladly paid $30.

Down the block a bobhaired livewire no older than 19 with a big diamond ring showed us a cracked toilet she patched with putty and said to take out the one upstairs with it. We drove out and picked up two. I helped Stanley bring them in and carry one up. It took two hours to change them. She paid $240 like it was nothing and I helped him lug the old ones out.

A block over we were shown a plugged sink from a toothpaste cap. Unable to plunge it down he scooted in tight under the pipes and opened things up underneath, the strain rising to his forehead. We were there twenty minutes and he took $10.

We had a referral to go see but he said he was going to LaGrange. Adding what he made minus cost of parts he handed me $25. He might have commented on how we worked but he was a dour soul, born that way I guessed. It had little to do with catching his wife with a black man.

'Okay so far?'

'Long as it lasts.'

I thought we could work through the neighborhood, come back around and go through again, such was my notion of plumbing repair.

I made two more appointments and called it a day. Working men would soon sit down to eat, Chicago dinner hour five, where in Louisville it was six.

I went for a red hot, sat in the pool hall until dark and drove back to Emil's, paying a dollar and waiting outside for Stanley to pull up. I said we had two appointments plus the referral, a good start. Upstairs he sat on the bunk with the buttcan between his feet. Other than his handsome face and plumbing skills I could not guess one thing a woman would see in him.

We went morn to the first referral and finished in two hours taking $50. Half down the block Stanley worked first under a drain, then went across the street and replaced valves on a water tank. A woman next door called us in to sweet-talk Stanley. I didn't care to leave him with her but had to find more work.

Finished there he said she paid $10, though he'd been there over an hour. We went to a house at the corner, coming out with $25. Called back across the street he refit a faucet on a bathtub, then we drove to the hardware store and brought back a toilet and showerhead. He put them in and the woman paid $160 and gave us a referral to go to Saturday.

Dumping the old toilet we returned to Emil's before five. Bunkers saw Stanley settle with me behind the truck. My part $40, I followed him in and paid for a night.

Friday eve it was and though I had a taste for a red hot I went instead to a Cermak diner for a plate of spaghetti and garlic bread. It wasn't Granme's spaghetti – far from it – but hit the spot like all Greek diner food. I'll say that for them.

I sat awhile. We had one referral and no appointments but with people home Saturday we could make a day of it. Back to Emil's I went upstairs and saw Irv there in a powwow over nickel-dime poker. Stanley sat smoking. He had not in that time taken off his shoes. I picked up Tike and gave him a going over.

'Hey there, Kingfisher.'

Irv looked over his glasses. 'How *tricks?*'

'What tricks?'

'I hear you got Stanley going for twenty percent.'

He thumbed an old deck. 'Kingfisher's been here all of two weeks and already has a bite on Stanley's pay. What else you got figured?'

Stanley said not a word for me. It was his nature and that does not change.

Morn he laid around until nine. Emil would not have taken that off anyone else. I waited outside and we drove to the referral. Finishing there by 11 he lit a cigarette at the back of the truck and handed me $8.

'I don't need nobody standing around while I work.'

'I make appointments. You don't have to drive to LaGrange. I help you out.'

'I still don't need nobody standing around.'

'Irv convinced you not to work with me?'

'I convinced myself.'

I put $8 in my pocket and walked back to my vehicle.

The year turned. I got a day or two a week at the record shop and went looking for more. Starting various jobs I developed another habit – quitting.

I worked in a beef lamb shop taking cuts out of the case, bundling them in paper and string. A rosy-cheeked Polish man (most of them are) talked to me like to the other counter men and made sure I was given a good sandwich and cold soda for lunch. My head only an inch above the meatcase, the customer usually short, as older women in the neighborhood were, we could not see one another and it started to get me. The Polish man did not want me to quit. He liked how quickly I learned the cuts and moved around, and that my fingers were not yellow from cigarettes, but he could not talk me out of it.

It wasn't just that I barely saw over the counter, but that some of the counter men had been there thirty years and I wondered was this the best they could do – not to go out in the world but to traverse long years a narrow cement aisle selling cuts to neighborhood women?

I got a job working for a portrait photography studio. Three quick buck artists from Boston had the business figured in tiers: photography, telephone solicitation, sales. The sign in front invited children for free photography. Afterward a phoner made appointments for a salesman to come and offer varous portfolios that could be made up. Prices went up to $99 and I received 25 percent of every portfolio I sold.

Making $275 for myself in no time I felt if I learned portrait photography I could go into business for myself. I would not so quickly have thought of going solo but the three young Bostons talked fast and if you didn't pick it up the first time they got hotheaded. I did not feel at ease around them.

I was making as many as 15 stops a day and selling mostly $24.99 packages. Regarded with suspicion because I was part Negro, I managed to win families over, feeling almost like an entertainer. Part of my presentation was to have them thinking I adored their children which showed because I loved small children more than all else. I went to a flat where the woman was obviously scared. It was on the second floor straight across from a limestone cathedral. She answered the door with two toddlers. Decor bleak, as usual in that neighborhood, she led me to a table where an infant sat in a high chair. I swung off my jacket to get started. As I presented her with pictures of the toddlers, they came to my side. I picked them up to show them, too. Sitting them on my legs, her jaws clenched and she pushed the pictures back.

Left thinking she was touchy I gave it no more thought. When I got back to the studio Seth said a priest called to say I acted inappropriately at a parishoner's home, that I took off my jacket and sat down without being asked and put two small kids on my lap. It was mostly true I said. His two partners stopped to stare. He told me from then on I was to take no liberties and stay within the guidelines of my training. Then he seemed to soften. I doubted it was in sympathy, I was bringing in money. Thinking it over I quit next morn. He got angry, suggested I had something to hide and didn't pay me all I had coming.

Next I had, according to my boss, the hardest job in all Creation – collecting bills from deadbeat niggers. I went up on a porch and a Negro with pink lips and a big belly put a gun to my head. I ran off the porch and out the gate with his white wife after me in her bathrobe yelling 'Come back. My husband's pullin' on his pants. He wants to fight you.'

Having tasted the wages of incentive I did not want to work for flat pay. My bunk was a dollar. Other than a red hot eve I got by on a container of cottage cheese and a piece of fruit and could easily go a day without. I stayed sturdy and clean in that I'd been raised to make the most of my food and to toilette using as little water as possible. Emil did not provide a shower. I searched the newspaper for jobs that did not look like fronts for fraud. I did not want to deceive. A jobber from the rail docks came to the pool hall to recruit strong backs to unload boxcars. I came forth and he said no. I asked for a chance and he took me with two others, soon seeing I was best. When he wasn't looking the two huddled to smoke. I kept going, thinking as I worked, correctly crossing off deliveries.

I started taking things for granted which someone in Chicago with usually no more than $20 in his pocket should not do. It is a town that will turn on you like its weather and it came at a time when I thought I was okay. I'd made $100 from unloading boxcars three straight days, but as Christmas neared my roadster stalled. At a garage many at the pool hall went to, the mechanic said it would cost $80 to fix, but when a part in an old car goes bad a compensating part soon follows. Handed a bill pared down to $120 I did not have a full dollar left for a bunk. It was Christmas Eve but the thought of asking Emil to let it go one night was forbidding. I had seen him turn on others, cussing them in his Slavic tongue. I did not want to shame myself by being cursed out, nor did I want to ruin a 'good Chicago thing.' The pool hall thinned out early, closing eight instead of twelve.

Even Greek coffee shops were dark. Cruising up down Cermak I stopped in the light of an appliance store and put on extra socks, wrapping Granme's quilt around twice. My toes prickling I went to urinate between buildings every hour or so, cowering there awhile blocked from wind. Doubled over I watched a small vehicle pull up. A voice carried, *'There!'*

Me thinking someone intended Christmas charity the window lowered on a fat bearded hippie aiming a camera. Shocked by two flashes in my eyes I watched the vehicle speed away.

I made the night, walking up and down Cermak, not letting my leg go numb or it would start to mortify. Warming up the car I held my toes to the vent until the pool hall opened.

It was Christmas but coffee was not on the house. Sleeping where I sat I was awakened by an old Slav who oft picked out something to point to in the newspaper. I followed his thick finger from Mayor Daley and family in front of their Christmas tree, down the page to a pitiful figure stooped in shadow, eyes bugged out in the night, inscribed: *The Wretched.* Wiley old DP he kept poking it was me.

Starting the year I tried various jobs, most of them I heard of at the pool hall. I worked in a liquor store in a gray waistcoat, sporting a feather duster at my hip. I buffed floors in an old office building and that was $8 for a quick two hours early eve. I sorted clothes at Salvation Army, easygoing there but donated piles formed fumes I could not get used to.

Spring and summer passed. Turning cold again, I stayed in the pool hall Sundays watching football. Loiterers like me stood back at the wall while in front fives and tens changed hands in one way or another on every down.

I took interest in it – a war basically, a war over land that took to the air like television voices said. As the Dauphin I felt I was gifted with second sight and saw what others did not. Betting $10 in a chance to win $200 by picking points winners in a six-game parlay, I lost six weeks in a row, missing out by one or two games. Turning to individual bets I lost oft as not, coming to the conclusion there is a part of the game that can be sure to no one, that being the players that Sunday most hardbitten to take or hold a length of field.

I got two days a week at a liquor store on Cermak. Keeping shelves full was piecemeal, unlike a grocery market where you shelve a box at a time. The owner and I were on our feet from nine to nine, two of us and a dog he kept under the counter for protection but what protection he expected from that animal I had no idea. Its spine was curved. I believe it had consumption. It choked on what it ate and out back twisted half around to defecate in squirts. I looked at this cursed creature, wondering if it knew when a little one, curled up with brothers and sisters to the warmth of a mother's belly, it would never know a home or be trusted with a child, or run in the blue under the eye of a gentleman but come into the hands of an old Chicago ogre, shut under a counter from light of day, unable to stretch its length or stand its height, and live hollow-cheeked and quivering, too blind to look into light – and be passed off as a German Shepherd. Why I stayed on six months haunts me more than all else. I should not have finished the day I started.

Six years went by. The *Groneg* idea for hospitals came and went for I saw no way to it. I didn't get to bottling HG9, shaming at the thought of going to skid row and asking old bums to come urinate in a bucket. Those two things weren't

138

going to work without some luck and I had begun to suspect that one must be born with it for it hardly changes.

Sans enterprise day is slow yet night comes before you know it. I bunked at Emil's but turned homeward to the pool hall, whether I worked or not, to sit looking at a television which played one channel, a slate of news and old variety shows of 1950s entertainers. Answering to no one, unbothered by want or what lay unfinished, I could hardly relive a day and slept dreamless, holding only in mind if Charlene ever gave a thought to where I'd gone. Here there I didn't go to Emil's but slept out back and washed at the toilet sink. I was healthy enough, hardy with good digestion and elimination and to this day am unable to fathom giving over to malaise or undicipline or an ether. I tried to throw it over like bad sleep but woke to no reveille. I wondered if it was self-inflicted even though the last thing I ever suspected was I was not of right mind.

Not changed much it seemed, no different in mirror, I sat down in a dime store for complimentary portrait, returning to lengthened forehead softer chin deepened eyes, an adult face though I still had grown no whiskers. It saddened not in vainglory but that it came with lost years.

What partly found me myself was a library visit, coming across what I long hoped for, an article on Japanese surgery that straightened and lengthened legs. Long bones were broken in two places, stretched apart then stationed by stints allowing space between segments to fill in with new bone and marrow, thereby lengthening. Trip and surgery with closeby convalescence cost $50,000 in all for two legs. I imagined it a good deal less for one. The Chicago working man was making near $500 a week. Taking steady employment along with moonlighting weekends I could save $30 thousand in a few years since my expenses were near nothing. I would also benefit that in a few years the surgery might to some degree

139

prove itself safe or dangerous, for I imagined it frightful to go far away and chance having a leg split and stretched.

I took off the brace and put it in the trunk. It had done no good I could see. My left leg neither strengthened nor straightened I felt I had lugged the brace for nothing. I bought new shoes, had the left heel built up and walked no worse.

Even in new hope I could not wholly rid myself of the haze or trance I liken to something I heard tell at the pool hall. An old prizefighter or faker posing as one – Chicago chockfull – told of being knocked down in Oakland. The punch did not hurt, felt rather good. He picked up the count and the referee was in no hurry, but he rested on a haunch fine with it. True or no I recognized those words like one does an old acquaintance from afar.

Going on my eighth Christmas in Chicago I found myself without a dollar for Emil's bunks. The pool hall closed early. Out at the curb I glimpsed a $20 bill in the gutter under the lamp. I did not jump. Greek coffee shop owners put a fake twenty folded in half under the mint cup. A customer fingering it out was treated to FUCK YOU on the other side. I picked it up expecting no better but it was real enough, whatever it was, and good for Christmas and a week ahead. It was not peculiar that when I was most needy something came along to hold me up.

My birthdate, February 2, I went to the record store. Usually giving me a day or two, he had nothing and said he would be closing up. I called Eddie at the rail dock, who said he might have work Friday. Looking through classifieds I drove downtown to an interview with a portrait company I understood offered commission work. I sat down with two men who said they had better, franchises with territorial rights, benefit of weekly newspaper ads and radio spots: priced $5000.

Friday I called Eddie who said he still had nothing to unload. Up down Cermak I walked, my day's work. Returned to the pool hall counting what I had left in my pockets, I overheard the new wrestling show at the armory on 51st was looking for a ring announcer. Occasionally I sat with DPs watching TV 'wrestling' from New York: braggarts buffoons behemoths belting out schoolyard animosities. Little interest I took but what more could the job be than presenting a contest, that simpler than other presentations I had made. Smoothing a blouse from my trunk I put on a necktie and went to see.

Come upon an old hangar on a lot the size of a football field, I parked under a banner that read *Hy Speed Promotions* and followed a cement walk to open double doors off the corridor, stepping into the *rear* in 'wrestling' lingo. A weight bench on a platform held up steel discs the size of railcar wheels. A crude voice going a mile a minute on the phone, I glanced into an off-side office and recognized late-night TV pitchman Hy Speed who hawked parcels of Arizona dessert at $99 an acre. Waiting to introduce myself I was confronted by a meter hack called Cully who wrote tickets up down Cermak but went about unharmed because he stooged for old rawboned cop Sarge Biltz with a reputation he could make it hard for you around Cermak. When Biltz made the rounds yeggmen and hop-fiends went out back. Returned to the counter he was slipped a fiver under his coffee cup.

'I'm here about the ring announcer position.'

'What's he want?' called Hy Speed from his desk.

'The announcer job,' said Cully.

'Tell him to sit.'

'He's not what you want.'

'Tell him to sit.'

Chicago vendors coming and going, I listened to his piggish squeals when they didn't see things his way. Making terms, take it or leave it, he dismissed them. Betweenwhile he and Cully sat shooting the breeze. I finally stood up to leave, when Cully edged an eye out the door.

'In here.'

I soon faced husky Chicago hustler Hy Speed. A shiny noggin hard as a nut, like many a Chicago huckster half along his nails were manicured. Two cigarettes neat at his lacquered fingertips looked his ration.

'What makes you think you can work for me? You've done public hawking, tent shows?'

'I knocked on doors. I have strong will to present.'

'Present what?'

'Present a product against an individual's will to resist.'

He eyed Cully.

'You know him?'

'He's a mooch. He sits in the pool hall all day watching everybody go by. I hear he sleeps out back. He's scared of his own kind. Go to Englewood, *go* mooch there!'

Hy Speed sat back with a smoke. To this day I'll say an honest-to-goodness blowhard won't be swayed from his instincts. He pointed to a poster. 'Call the first match.'

Knowing the nature of television wrestling I all but clicked my heels, calling out in singsong developed in prayer.

'Hy Speed Promotions presents a night of Championship Chicago Wrestling!' I pointed right. *'First fall, twenty-minute time limit. In red corner at 208 pounds, the Saginaw Sawmill, Cleeton Flowers!'*

I swiveled opposite like throwing a cape on my back. *'In blue corner at 220 pounds, late of French Foreign Legion, infamous coldblooded Colonel Petan!'*

He was not displeased.

'Hy Speed Promotions has no neutrals. Every swinging dick pays for himself. A Hy Speed player builds his character, gives all, fears nothing. I see you a sharpie in sharkskin inviting suspicion from the suckers for your superior tone. Simple bastards, verbally abused all their lives, they will take from your arrogance your contempt for them. You'll side with a jobber – a weak character – against a marquee – a premium guy. You'll run the deck, pound the mat and hamstring marquees. That will get you chased. You're scrawny and gimp on one side. Rough-and-tumble is what it takes.'

'I am fast in playacting and roughhouse well for my size and stature. May I ask the pay?'

'Twenty-five smackers. We go on TV you'll pull down three hundred a gig and perks. You like girls? You're not *queer?*'

'I am not.'

He wrote up the back of a business card. 'Colonial Suits on 61st, tell Chazz I sent you.'

Thinking I was in luck I drove west and came in on a strict little Italian his hands behind him like a military martinet. Presenting the card front and back I followed him to a rack where he picked out a charcoal sharkskin. I well knew a savvy suit buyer gives but a casual look, revealing little of his first impression. Not asking he pinned the sleeves.

Changed to the pants to pin the cuffs, I posed in full-length mirror, never having imagined myself so sleek. His Argentine assistant, the flag on his lapel, – I knew the flags – added a blouse of pearl shell color. I went to the counter where Chazz punched the register to $220.

I flicked the business card over.

'Hy Speed Promotions pays.'

'Pays *what?* You don't have money?'

'Just the card.'

He dialed the number.

'Chazz, Colonial Suits. A guy here says you're paying for his suit?'

I was given Hy on the phone.

'In case you don't know, pal, you swing your own getup.'

'I don't have $220.'

'You don't have the job. Make an arrangement. Don't come back without it.'

143

I returned to the pool hall thinking it hadn't been a waste for I felt good at how the sharkskin looked on me. Usually I parked in back but Friday eve the lot was full. A small red convertible with a Kentucky plate out at the curb was a tempting target, but breaking into a car behind the pool hall put you at risk. Small thieves were shelacked back there by bigger thieves. The back door was always open with someone stepping out to smoke. Eight o'clock I went out and saw an opening. Swinging out in reverse into alley into the lot, I cut someone off in the dark.

Two known armed robbers followed me in, a Mexican over six foot and a Southern hoodlum in front.

'You're quick in that car.'

'I will move if I cut you off.'

'You a Kentucky boy?'

'Louisville.'

'Harlan County.'

'I know of it.' I did not say what.

'I see you beatin' up and down the street. You lookin' for work?'

'I do honest work if you know of any.'

'We need a driver tonight.'

'Whereto, may I ask?'

'Hundred fifty miles south.'

'Using my vehicle?'

'Ours, you drive.'

'Why do you need me?'

He looked sad a moment.

'My sister got into prostitution when she was fifteen. I had her tracked to a house downstate. We're taking her out tonight and need a hand.'

'You expect trouble?'

'We're not taking no for an answer if that's what you mean?'

'What does it pay?'

'More than sittin' here.'

I scratched my head. 'You're not leading me on? I don't have much.'

'Hang in, we deal square. I'm Isaac, he's Manuel.'

Honest face Isaac's, but the old Creole says that amongst thieves he of the honest face is the biggest thief of all. We went to a vehicle seven eight years old. The trim was off, hard to tell a Chevy or Dodge or the color in the dark for I of royal blood was to a degree color blind. Its thrum shook my elbows. I had known only a gentle motor. Gripped on the wheel I was pointed south through industry with hearth fires in the night.

Out on US1 along empty fields I came of mind they meant to leave me and go back for my pony. The Mexican dialed the old teenager music, a song he lamented.

'Santo and Johnny! My girl and me used to grind to them. Nights in El Monte, old tunes on the radio – they were your wheels your girl your job your morality even. I turned twenty I joined up. "Wait for me, baby," I asked her. She waited alright. *"Next!"'*

He looked back at Isaac hiding his face.

'The Lord never touched your soul, you feel for no one.'

'The Lord spoke to me once but it was in Spanish. I couldn't understand what the hell he was saying.'

Manuel stroked my arm.

'Keep the Lord of Israel in your heart – he will make you glad as he will shame the promotion of fools.'

An hour on I pulled off into dirt track.

'Blink the lights.'

Flicked on and off they glimpsed a farmhouse ahead.

'Enough!'

I kept an eye in the mirror as Isaac opened the trunk, unscrewed the plate, screwed on another and came around to change the front. Out of the dark a long Chevy drew up, the driver and I exchanging looks. It took little to see this individual was contributing nothing to society. Shoving off he wheeled out on highway. Isaac got back in.

'Get after him.'

Making now they meant me no harm, we were going to rescue his sister. Swinging out in reverse I tailed the Chevy to town limits, coming upon an ancient brick armory and two men going up steep stairs along solid wall. Turning across a culvert into a wide parade lane I moved along cars parked on both sides and pulled over leaving the engine running. Across parade grounds I made out the highway we came on. Isaac leaned up on my shoulder.

'You'll be here for us?'

I tapped his hand. 'With all my heart!'

Going to the trunk they concealed weapons under their jackets. Makeshift truncheons I took them for. The Mexican stuck his head back in.

'Hang in like Errol Flynn.'

Turned over my shoulder I watched them go back up the lane across the culvert, cross paths with the contact on the front walk and hurry up the cement stairs aside the wall. My heart full I was part of a rescue of a girl from evil, took it hellish wheels to spirit her away I was their man. Counting minutes in my head I had to go out behind a tree and had not finished urinating when startled by a door banging open against steel rail. A gunshot would not have matched its call. The contact staggering back on the walk, Isaac and the Mexican came running down the stairs and across the culvert, no girl with them but the Mexican swung a sack. Getting back behind the wheel I had never seen such running. Heels chiming like picks on cement, they jumped in. What I thought batons or crowbars were rifles abbreviated at barrel and stock. The contact's vehicle whipped by in a gust.

'Where's your sister?'

'*Vamoose! Go!*'

With a lurch I chased the long Chevy sweeping across open field, rumbling toward highway. Turning onto US1 I switched on the lights and wheeled around a semi truck. Ten miles on I was pointed into the same dirt lane, coming up on the contact outside his vehicle. Isaac got out with the sack to do some business with him on the Chevy hood. Finished he changed the plates back and tucked the rifles in the trunk.

Swinging out in reverse I asked nothing, recalling a course in Common Law, taking from it there had been no notion on my part to rob and steal, not that it would do me much good in front of a rural Illinois jury.

They said nothing on the way back. Pulling around behind the pool hall I was handed my pay.

'Don't let us hear nuthin'.'

Getting into the pony I counted ten twenties, exonerating myself they came not through sin but chance, unclean money from unclean hands of no rightful owner. It could sure go awhile but the sharkskin came to mind. Since the time I worked for Mel I promised myself a beautiful suit one day, and taking pride in one might finally be the physic to rid me of the malaise I could not completely throw over.

Saturday midnoon I drove to Colonial Tailors. Counting ten twenties two tens Chazz said the cuffs would be done by five. At a counter nearby I determined that if I took the wrestling announcer job I could make the cost back in nine Saturdays not losing weekday time.

Returned I donned sharkskin and pearl-shell blouse, having a look in the mirror before heading to the armory. Hy Speed was in his side office with his front man, Red Canyon, a ponderous Southern character in ten-gallon hat and string tie.

Presenting myself at the door Hy Speed said. 'Peg the legs and get hornrim glasses. See the picture: pegged pants, hornrims – I want you looking like illegitimate spawn Sammy Davis, Jr. had with a white woman?'

I sat down on a bench thinking I might be on a winning streak. Wrestlers arrived in dark glasses with bags of take-out, looking like they had lain around all day. They wore no buttoned shirts zippered pants laced shoes, but togs with drawstrings and either skimpy slip-ons or unscuffed work boots. Doffing their tops they munched barechested. This group was obviously the marquees, the overdogs.

A second group not as ripe took some old lockers on the side. Used as fodder – beaten down cursed humiliated – they finished each match on the canvas. All had a defeated look except for one in purple outfit with velvet jacket and monogrammed wrestling boots. Cheering others up, he came to me.

'You the new announcer?'

'Daupin.' I stood up.

'Up'n'Up Barry.'

He spoke rolling his shoulders, rocking on the balls of his feet.

'You've been at this awhile?'

'Breaking in. I come weekdays to work with marquees. My old man is the biggest marble and granite dealer in Chicago. I'm there all day he says or I'm out. I'm gonna live his humdrum life, talking up cuts of stone? Muscle sells. The public worships muscle. Muscle is business. People in top fields revere muscle.'

He meant marquees. 'They get comped all over Chicago, do out-of-towners: Elgin Joliet Rockford, gigs at conventions and car shows, pull down bucks and got women in reserve. Black Satin went nationwide. Women after him all the time, he had to shake them. A judge's wife came by in her Cadillac to catch him here.'

Called to Hy Speed I was handed a page of match-ups with stars next to marquee names.

'Sell *sizzle* sell *smoke!* No steak for suckers.'

Out in the corridor I made up enhancements to wrestlers' names, going by the sound of them. Hy Speed barreled by with Red Canyon who looked the size of a crate from the belt down. I had not in my life seen such ponderous haunch. Following them into the arena to a bell table set back from ringside I took mic and cord. When not bellowing through a speaker Red Canyon was short of breath with Southern man turkey-gobble. 'Unloop going up, reloop going out or you'll trip on your head. I go *"Heyho, Let's Go!"* you get on the stick.'

I climbed the stoop into the ring, getting the feel of mat and rope, thumping a finger on the mic as I'd seen others do. *Hullo! Hullo!*

Like carnival-goers grownups arrived with whole broods, followed in by chortling teenagers and local loudmouths. Young floozies sashayed in twos threes vying for vulgar hoots in tight jeans. As they went by I was sorry for them that they felt compelled at tender age to paint and flaunt themselves. Arena half full Hy joined Red Canyon at the bell table. Pointed up I unlooped the cord climbing back through the ropes and stepping front center. Arena dimming, hot lights popped above the ring. Red Canyon bellowed *'How ya'll t'night? Ya'll ready for rasslin'?'*

The referee led a scruffy jobber down the ramp into the ring followed by a highstepper in Foreign Legion cap, waist jacket and tails.

'Heyho, Let's Go!'

The half house cheered back.

Ring light beating down I held my head back, calling out like the newsboy of old radio dramas with hand cupped to mouth.

'Welcome to Championship Chicago Wrestling presented by Hy Speed Promotions. First match, twenty-minute time limit, in red corner at 200 pounds, the Moline river runt, Muskrat Joe!'

149

Through howls imitating my yodel I faced left.

'In blue corner, admitting allegiance to no land or flag, only to those who pay him to march and die, the infamous coldblooded Colonel Petan.'

I climbed down looking to the bell table to see if Hy liked it but he was gone. The bell rang. Taking runs at one another Petan took over, entrapping Muskrat's head between his 'delts and traps' (armpit) and squeezing like a nutcracker. Obviously no man could withstand it. Muskrat flounced at the constriction of blood to his brain, flailing he could stand no more.

Next came Up'n'Up Barry and bronze Kilowatts the color of a new penny from artificial blue light. To Up'n'Up Barry I added *'Chicago's man of marble and granite!'* to Kilowatts, *'Peoria Powerhouse!'* Kilowatts broke clean from the first lock-up and stuck out his hand. Through howls of distrust Barry took it only to be cuffed by the other. Legs wobbling he was run post to post, turned upside down and slammed into the mat until he waved surrender. Dropped on his head he stumbled back to his feet, exiting to cheers for sportsmanship.

Third match featured Big Fat Slob, his game he was institutionalized, shy of adults but loved and protected children. His opponent, a pale Negro calling himself YMCA Kid, didn't look right in the head to me. In the back he'd slapped over both shoulders as though fleas buzzed about his ears. He had YMCA muscles alright but was not half the size of Slob. Following my call he made blind charges Slob fended off, then was taken by the head to have it repeatedly slammed into a ring post pad. The house picked up a count so rote that when Slob's hand slipped YMCA slammed his head himself.

Back forth rear to front Hy detoured to me.

'Look at the beating your brother's taking. Help him! Grab Slob's leg, trip him up.'

On the pool hall TV I oft saw side characters make pests of themselves to distract hero wrestlers from their work. Hurrying ringside I protested Slob's tactics. Facing Kid around in the stoop corner he belly-slammed him until it looked as though Kid would succumb from asphyxiation. Pulling myself up to the mat I ducked my head through the ropes and from the side grabbed Slob's boot for Kid to get free. Slob stomped twice, bouncing me away. Finishing the match he flopped on Kid and stomped out.

Next I pestered supposed motorcycle hoodlum Jackanapes running Cleeton Flowers around the ring. Beating him to the corners I swiped at his boots until he timed me and swung one boot across the other grazing my chin. Ropes trembling he leaned over the top.

'Come again I'll break your hips and legs.'

I stood back astonished that but for the bottom rope I would have been kicked in the face.

Ending near 11 o'clock, Red Canyon stood up bellowing to bring family and neighbors. Back in the rear I thought wrestlers would introduce themselves. Only Up'n'Up Barry came, asking me to keep calling him the man of marble and granite.

Hy Speed paid at the end of the show wanting to keep wrestlers around in case the house got out of control, which from their dull look I did not think likely. Showing my face he flicked away two tens a five like it was a waste.

Content to have made up some cost of the suit, I wanted to get all I could out of it. Doubting female companionship would come my way of a chance meeting, I took a notion to become acquainted at a Sunday worship. Reverend Brown in Louisville oft mentioned twin brother Roy in Chicago. I went to a directory and found Rev. Royal Brown at a private residence and Christian Unity, both on Homestead Rd. out at city limits.

Too late to get a bunk at Emil's I changed out of the sharkskin and dozed in Granme's quilt until the pool hall opened at six. Washing up at the toilet sink, I changed back, sat a few hours over coffee, then drove west, coming to a chapel in an area of fields. Parking behind other vehicles I went forth treated with suspicion. Many a stranger come to black worship in slick get-up has won over good people, then proved himself a trickster to one in particular – a lonely sister.

Reverend Brown greeted arrivals with his better half, so alike his Reverend brother I would have mistaken them after eight years. Bid welcome I did not reveal myself of Louisville. Prayers conducted the way I remembered it I took up song without looking in the book.

The reverend's sermon on the eternal split of Jacob and Essau, by now my eyes were on a flirtatious member of the choir. Big boned, red toned like Charlene with strong glasses and protruding teeth, when her robe split I had not yet seen such proud legs with full round calves and heels – white women's legs scarce in black women, such few called *redbones* and *stallions* by black layabouts who have nothing better to do all day than sit around and make up names.

Out back for refreshments choir mates called her DiJi. Bertha the organ player complimented me on my strong clear call, inviting me to join song practice. Back inside I took side to DiJi. Friendly she was but eyes only for tall dark men there.

Returned to the pool hall for nowhere better, I went for a red hot, coming upon one local telling another of a nightwatchman opening at a food bank on Adams Road, no more it was than to sit around and sleep. Out that way first thing morn, I asked at service stations for direction to a food bank. Come to a metal hangar I went inside, made application and took a booklet on night man procedure with a Maywood address stamped on back to go to. Reading it through I drove west to a State office and took a test on a clipboard. Checking my answers the proctor pressed on the State seal. Quickly I returned with it to the food bank. Impressed by my speed the supervisor took me to a phone on the wall by the roll gate, pointing to red and blue call buttons.

'Fire and police, no other line goes out. You get rung once a night, you don't answer another call comes ten minutes after; don't answer that you'll be let go. Don't slip out. You're here in case of fire. Smoke gets thick all foodstuffs are condemned and sold to Central America for pennies.'

Giving me a heavy gold badge he showed me laundered work shirts, advising to wear a new one each night and throw it in the hamper morning. He opened a refrigerator holding a block of cheese jar of mustard loaf of bread.

'Help yourself but break no container on the line.' He pointed to a bin of damaged cans packages. 'See something you like, eat it cold. Bring no hot plate, clean up after yourself, leave nothing around.'

I was shown a corner with a nozzle overhead and drain below. 'Burn shower. Run it every night or the water gets rusty.' A final word, 'It's for loners who like it.'

I came back at 9:45 and Omar the afternoon boss told me to drive my vehicle up the ramp to center track. He pulled the gate down and left out the side. I went to the back, put on shirt and badge and straightened the place up, which I was not told to do. I scrubbed the sink wiped down the table stomped down the trash. Letting the burn shower run I ran a push broom down center track, sweeping the length.

Washing my hands, I got out the cheese and bread, read a few magazines and put my head on the table. Looking up at the clock I determined that if I were going to sleep I would do it right. Putting cardboard flats on the floor near the phone I lay down on my side. Rung after three I shook awake.

'*I'm here!*'

'Just checkin'.'

Sleeping another hour I got up to wash at the sink asking myself what difference would it make when I ran the burn shower if I was underneath? Soap and industrial paper towels to dry off with, I let the water run again. It did not get warm but I soaped up and rinsed off more refreshed than I had felt in years. I had taken advantage in a fair way I thought. An hour to go I took wet towels to my pony and wiped it down.

The gate rolled up, crew and supervisor arriving daybreak. At his nod I wheeled down the ramp with a day's time, night's sleep, fed and showered. Up Adams Road I saw a sign on a pole: DOG BOY WANTED. An arrow pointed up a short hill to a fenced patch with hovels circled like studs on a sundial. A dog was chained to a peg in front of each, tethered far enough for it to nose around but not to get together. The proprietor worked under a canvas hangar refurbishing furniture. A fit individual wearing steel rim safety glasses, he showed what he expected of me each day and let me at it. First I shoveled up droppings and dropped them in a barrel. Next I opened five cans of Vets at both ends, pushing out a roll of meat, slicing it in two, parting each half to a bowl with dry meal, mashing it together and putting it out.

After it was gobbled up I wiped and rinsed the bowls then leashed two dogs at a time for a twenty-minute walk, bringing them back to a bench where I gave a light brushing that took to noon. The proprietor went to his vehicle saying he would be back in an hour. By his bearing he looked retired from a good position, possibly in the military. I took it he was going to meet friends or associates. I didn't think he was stopping home because there was a trailer by the hangar I took it he slept in.

When he returned I drove off bethought of more I could do there. A blind beagle and tall white hound choked on the chow. It occurred to me to bring dented cans of corn and peas from the food bank bin to mix with meat and meal so it might be swallowed easier. I had seen a crushed box of cotton tips in the bin I could use to clean eyes ears as well as mine. Instead of walking them around the patch I would lead them out the gate and up down the hill to exert pull on chest and legs.

Next day Phillip watched through his silver rims as though he was not pleased. Spare in habit he might have thought his customers getting too much for their money. Strict men can be almost as opposed to that as they are to shortcoming.

I finished the week at the patch Friday midnoon, at the Food Bank Saturday morn, paid cash at the former by check the latter. Sleeping on cardboard flats there as good as on any bunk I rolled out into first light showered and rested, feeling it was my private abode which for all purposes it was.

Going to the pool hall for a sweet roll and coffee I sat all morn until I asked myself if there wasn't something better and drove to the rail docks where Eddie had four hours for me. Paid $12 I stopped for a red hot earlier than usual then drove to the armory.

Hy Speed was in the office with a gentleman in a tuxedo I knew from Channel 9 News, Terry Donley, who according to station advertisement had been there since 1949 and was phasing into retirement. Seventy now, a fine figure of a man he was with a head of silver hair.

Marquees arrived in eyeshades, ogling themselves in full-length mirror before they sat down to take-out barechested as they liked. Changing into the sharkskin I sorted rank among them that went by who had formed the ripest muscle. Wrestlers sans tanned leathery muscle they deemed 'doughboys.' First out of them was a new lifting technique or product to increase size of this horny formation they prized.

Second topic was moneymaking at openings and fests where they painted on smiles as greeters. They also took jobs that paid a 'C-note' at dance clubs, doing not much more than 'mugging' at the door.

After that they talked about big cars they drove of Lincoln Cadillac brands, followed by accounts of recent sexual episodes with muscle-worshiping females (skunks they called them) so vile they made me wonder how a woman could let herself do such things. They also kept company with well-heeled male admirers called kafabes who steered them to side gigs around town.

Life was their physiques, easy money, large vehicles and debauchery – 'getting over' in their words. Those with wives and children spoke of them only in complaint, some saying they had or would have themselves 'fixed.' Letting their food digest they swelled up at the weight bench letting out barnyard grunts and rough rectal blows. I asked myself how such characters could associate with everyday people, unaware they were no friends of anybody, referring to the public at large as 'moochers' to be had any way at hand.

Jobbers trailing in, there was a new one half again the size of any of the others, in red checkered lumberjack, roughened dungarees and boots.

Bringing two cups of coffee to the office Cully came to tell me I was history.

'Meaning what?'

'You're out. Terry Donley's the new announcer.'

'I work once, that's it?'

'Carny bylaw you're around till somebody better. Nuthin's keepin' you.'

I wanted to hear it from Hy. Ignoring me he presented Terry Donley to the Marquees. The old gentleman shook hands with buffoons barely clothed. Shaming for him I thought to leave. What use of Hy telling me? Obviously an insincere carny hustler he would not make it up to me. I could only count it as a lesson in dealing with those who demand a lot up front. Usually they mean you no good and take all the advantage. But I could not make myself leave just yet. I wanted to see how a television professional called a match.

I caught up with Hy heading for the front doors.

'Hy, you used me once, that's it?'

He swung around.

'I don't *know* you – develop your character, run the ring, show you can pay for yourself.'

Gate opened, Red Canyon welcomed one and all from the bell table. A half house settled in he rang the bell and introduced Terry Donley as the new Championship Wrestling announcer, a man known in Chicagoland homes thirty years now. The old gentleman went up into the ring wiping his brow.

A marquee and a jobber climbed into the ring. In tone of old radio calls Granme mama I had listened to, Terry Donley presented marquee Hiram Schnapps against Muskrat Joe.

The bout and next two went with the jobber taking quick advantage, then being cuffed mauled twisted and slammed flat. Around me eyes bugged out at heavy blows dealt to jobbers and hopefuls. Wondering why marquees weren't matched I determined they would not take such loud beatings from each other. The action would be like on the Saturday night show from New York where fists and stomps were seen coming a mile off. Look-alikes wouldn't fill seats here in this high hollow place. It would take echoing clouts and kicks, half real beatings to spread word of mouth around Chicago.

The new hopeful in the red lumberjack came down the ramp, going against Jackanapes the motorcycle hoodlum who tried to kick me in the face.

Terry Donley announced him: *'From the wilds of the North Country at 266 pounds, Yukon Kid!'* Off came his lumberjack, shoulders a fair yard across, back sloped, sides steep, fists round as hooves. At the bell he went at Jackanapes. Bent low he butted him like a goat while Jackanapes banged the heels of his fists down on his shoulder blades. Driven to his knees he rose up for Jackanapes to take his arm, kick up under his sternum and swing him corner to corner. Wheeling him Jackanapes flew off his feet. If this Yukon had wanted to he could have thrown him up over his back like a gunnysack. Ending with Jackanapes no longer able to steer him with any guise of reality he pushed him down on all fours and attacked from above hammering on his back until Yukon flattened out. Turning him over for the pin Jackanapes left the ring 'blown-out' in wrestling lingo. The lumberjack climbing back to his feet, I followed him up the ramp to the rear where he was accosted a second time by Jackanapes.

'I whip you into corners, numbnuts, don't flatfoot me. *Anticipate!* I got you by the arm, dance and sing. Get some footwork.'

Hy Speed come, Jackanapes turned on him. '*Where'd* you find this cockstrong son of a bitch – Burger King?'

I sat down by the new jobber and kept my voice low.

'You were on your hands and knees, he pounded your back, you could have been crippled.'

I didn't care he saw me odd.

'Why take hits on your spine? You sin to the strong body you were given. They don't care what they do to you. I think they would be known a crippler. I know not if you're a real lumberjack but I see in your hands you have been rough and ready. Why let them hurt you?'

Disturbed by what he had allowed upon himself I wanted to see no more. Returned behind the pool hall I changed out of the sharkskin and huddled in Granme's quilt until daybreak. Washing up I changed back and sat over coffee until I drove to the Unity.

DiJi's family had come up from rural Illinois. Her mother, a white woman came with DiJi's brother the color of a carrot. The one white person, she harped about white people back home to anyone who would listen while her round red spawn stood chin to chest. I thought him simple, but after song he charged out first to help himself to the spread in back.

I doubted a simpleton could be so fast on his feet. I brought DiJi a cup of ginger ale. Polite she was but annoyed.

'Daupin, I am a big girl with big body parts and need a man with big hands to handle them.'

Leaving me to myself she was told she was chosen from the choir to accompany Mrs. Nelson on a Unity tour through Kentucky Tennessee. She jumped up and down on those legs of hers like women do on television game shows.

Finishing a third week at the Food Bank and dog patch, savoring my positions there as blessings, I found nothing to do all Saturday and went to the armory to see if Terry Donley would keep coming to a job below his dignity.

He was in the side office with Hy Speed going over figures, his role there, I now took it, more than to call matches. The lumberjack character, Yukon, stood idly by while marquees billowed their chests by jerking the weight up and down at the bench, snubbed by those self-conscious of their knotty unnatural physiques in the presence, height and width, of a rawbone natural.

He was in the fourth match against the smallest marquee, L'l All-America, a crewcut acrobat in cowboy-style boots and stars and stripes on his trunks. Else a white forelock no other hair grew, even under his arms.

I went ringside. In the first three matches, jobbers, including Up'n'Up Barry, took clouts on neck shoulders and back before sprawling out.

Yukon Kid climbed into the ring, the house still not knowing what to make of him. Came L'l All-America, he the only marquee who spoke other than of personal gain, sounding off on the waste of tax dollars and welfare fraud. Against those things myself I was fooled by him and came to hear he did all he railed against. He paid no taxes, lived in common law, handled food stamps and even meal and taxi tickets meant for the lame and elderly. Small and quick his ploy was to be caught in a bear hug in the middle of the ring, mouth out to the crowd like trout jumping for a hook. Answering to cheers and stomps he flailed his limbs, slapping kicking jobbers up down, swiveling around behind them and riding their backs like a cowboy before rolling them boots over trunks for a pin.

Ringside Hy Speed caught sight of me.

'You sit here *free!* What'm I gettin' out of it? Get cracking or get the hell out! You can't think, run the ropes and bang your goddam head on a post! Crawl on your hands and knees, do *something!* He turned on Cully. 'He takes the best seat in the house; you and me run around like two idiots.'

Unwelcome in a seat I went to the stoop. I would have left once and for all but I wanted to see if Yukon right above took my advice. At the bell he went into his routine, lunging missing. Finally he bullied L'l All-America into a corner, slamming him into the post. Fists clenched overhead he banged down on his shoulders reducing him in height. Bending to blows L'l All-America was taken up in a bear hug and turned under ring lights to baste. As he hooted to the rafters, the house stomped up a din until he found strength to flail his arms and legs and break the hold. Yukon stumbling L'l All-America swung up on his back snatching his red ruff. Yukon tried to buck him off but L'l All-America jabbed rubber spurs in his sides and slapped him post to post, waving to all like a Wild West Show rider. Ridden to the stoop corner Yukon was red as fire. Asking myself when out of common decency the slapping would stop, I eased up the stoop as he turned Yukon around and rocked on his back. Poking my head through the ropes I snatched hold of his white suede boot with both hands and leaped back to the deck pulling him half off. Shrieks in my ears he jumped out of the ring and chased me around two corners before I swerved into a diagonal and ducked under the stands. Braced on toes and fingertips not to dirty myself, floorboards right above me rattling, L'l All-America stuck in his head, saw how deep I was in and spit in disgust. Swinging himself back over the ropes he finished the match with a series of drop kicks that left Yukon flat for the finisher, a belly dive from the top rope.

A jobber was to stay stretched out to show the devastation of the beating. Pulling himself to his feet Yukon trudged off. Following I expected L'l All-America to have something to say for the shrieks we raised. I did not yet know his true character.

I stepped into the rear and he flew in my face.

'Don't go behind me, *pal!* Don't come up on my back, buddy boy! You ain't been here long enough. Work in front of me, suckermouth. Try it again you'll be picking your teeth off the deck.'

I drove away with new smarts in dealing with a blowhard like Hy Speed should I come across one again. More importantly, after being around self-worshipers and simpleminded rabble who came to adore them I had renewed will to continue my education, to go into a second phase so to speak. Time and materials were available to me at the food bank, a bin of undelivered periodicals from the post office I could read from as I had read each day at Mel's.

Sunday night I read *National Geographic* the way I had read *Reader's Digest*, choosing sentences to put in my own words and discuss with myself their import. Finer wording than I was used to, the article took more than an hour to finish and another to settle in mind before I lay down on the flats. Morn I drove to the patch and tended to the dogs. Phillip leaving lunchtime I perused an old volume he had there, listing every breed classified in the world up to 1955. Taken by its illustration, I would come to know general height weight colors markings temperament, matching those in my care to such description.

Phillip ran a tidy business on a quarter acre, ordered and honest, how I liked things. A sportsman's Airedale had been there two weeks. He paid Phillip three twenties from his wallet which divided to $4.25 a day. Let's say ten dogs seven days brought $300, less cost of food. I imagined with half an acre I could board twenty thirty even forty.

A trait of these dogs puzzled me. What was it of Phillip and sportsmen come by that had them bowing and cringing in their presence, when they took me their kind caretaker for a nobody? What quality did arrogant white men have I did not? At the mere point of Phillip's finger a barker slinked to its hovel.

Reading at the food bank I occasionally turned on the employees' radio, listening Thursday night to a rebroadcast of a round-table of Chicago newscasters on the state of the profession. Terry Donley a panelist, it was poignant to me how he leavened the discussions of young opinionated broadcasters, with sage thought. I took a notion to go to the armory to ask if he might offer advice on how to break into the news game. Inclined to fact, willed to present, I saw in myself a public communicator, to even dare one day to be a leader in a newsroom, what with the forethought and enhancement I put into work.

Donning the sharkskin Saturday I drove to the armory coming upon a Channel 4 tractor-trailer and cable running to the arena to a command platform set up in a diagonal. Going back to the rear I was met by Up'n'Up Barry.

'We're going live! Everybody's on a Chicago Day Player Contract. Tough you missed out.'

Marquees were circled to discuss how to turn what would be presented to them to best advantage. At the other side jobbers looked dazed. They had taken beatings not for nothing. Tonight they would be on Chicago TV and paid good money.

Hy Speed came out of the office with Red Canyon, Terry Donley and a Channel 4 honcho.

'People, Hugo, our co-ordinator, has a few things to go over.'

An experienced man he didn't flinch from muscular marquees drawing around him.

'We go live tonight and next Saturday night for the possibility of putting on a weekly gig called *Saturday Night Showdown.*'

Marquees gave applause.

'Pay for now is $289 per Chicago Day Player Contract.'

Marquees were prepared to contest, L'l All-America as spokesman.

'All due, Hugo, some of us – me one – been at this some years going to podunk venues for no more than gas money, developin' skills, gainin' a followin' at cost to our bodies. Others here are green as grass. Channel 4 pays come-latelies contract, dandyfine, just give firstcomers their due.'

Marquees hurrahed!

Hugo wasn't moved. 'Channel 4 has no knowledge of your skills and followings. For now everyone pulls down the same.'

L'l All-America redoubled. 'Again all due, Hugo, ain't it what Communism's about, same pay unequal ability?'

Marquees gave warwhoops but Hugo kept them at arm's-length.

'I see it as everybody coming to the mark. The camera comes in tight. Don't turn on it. The operator's vulnerable with an eye to the finder. An attack on the camera is an attack on him. That said it's just another eye.'

Hy Speed took it up. '*Black Satin's* coming. Don't let him show you up. Go beyond yourself. Put one on!'

Making a homecoming after going national, Black Satin announced himself at the double doors as 'a man's fright, a whore's delight!' A smile twice any marquee's, he was with a white girl no older than twenty, though he looked forty. Thrilled as marquees were with themselves they deferred to him. Their undressing in front of the girl did not faze him. At the other end jobbers cowered. Black Satin went easy on no one. Even the girl looked hardused with bags under her eyes, like she caught a few from him now and then.

Coming ringside I watched Hugo up on the control platform with the Channel 4 announcer and long camera. Cable ran to a second camera ringside. It was no more complicated than Hugo giving directions to two camera operators as three jobbers including Up'n'Up Barry took beatings, pounded by resentful blows meted out for pulling down the same pay. Hugo flipped off his headphones and climbed down. Terry Donley left the ring. I would have stopped him a moment but he was perspiring from hot lights and I didn't want to delay him.

After the break I found myself by the stoop, the camera operator turning to me for no one better. The Yukon character went up in the ring and took off his lumberjack, his chest and shoulders like white marble under strong light. Then came Black Satin in blazed tuxedo pants and patent leather boots. I'd heard him say he was going to make his money fast which I took to mean the jobber would get a beating, getting in few if any licks and battered from the bell.

Prancing his fill his pants flew off. Chicago rabble half-wild at the return of this Black hero and old friend, Terry Donley called the match-up. The bell rang and Black Satin reversed Yukon's hold, bending him back into the ropes and letting him have it in hollow of neck and shoulder. Marquees did this with a cuffed hand but Black Satin threw flathanded, leaving welts. Laying in six, any one of which would break a normal man at the knees, he drove Yukon post to post, lighting into him anew. Swinging him around to the stoop corner he hopped up on the botton ropes, sending down clouts echoing like thunder claps. A useless referee stood off. Balanced on the bottom ropes Black Satin's patent leather boots were eye-level to me. Emboldened by the camera eye across the stoop I took hold of the rope and heaved back with all my strength tripping him up. All there jumped to their feet pointing it was me. Hopping back on as though to swoop down on me from above he paused to grin for the camera. I backed away expecting he would not bother with smallfry like me. Taking his ease on the ropes Yukon's eyes told me nothing. *Aaaagh!* Snatched on the shoulder I shot ahead from a rip of material with L'l All-America after me. Black Satin cut across the ring to head me off. Ears full of shrieks I fled round two corners into a diagonal and scrambled under the stands, flattening myself out. Ducking in his head L'l All-America cussed me all to hell.

I pushed back to my knees, a $200 suit damaged because of the need to squeeze every last penny out of everything. I coaxed myself there without enough sense to know I stood in danger of disturbed individuals who would gladly lay my head open.

Staying hidden until Red Canyon so-longed the rabble, I dusted myself off and inspected my jacket in and out. The torn lining could be sewn but the shoulder L'l All-America grabbed was stretched and I could never again think the sharkskin new. I would have been heartsick but for brave Haiti's fiercest admonition to its young – grieve naught not of flesh and blood – only that is human can't be regained. Waiting until vendors packed up I went to the rear. The marquees were gone. Yukon sat alone, a neck red with welts. I showed him the torn lining.

'You saw him steal up on me, I could have gotten away clean.'

He shrugged it was no business of his.

'I helped you. Black Satin was laying into you. You could have given a yell.'

Office open, Hugo sat at a folding table with a Channel 4 bookkeeper while Hy Speed counted the take. Looking like he wanted somebody to talk to, I thought he meant Yukon but it was me he called.

'That stunt tonight, was that coming?'

'I did it on impulse.'

'He's a mooch,' said Hy. 'I let him in free, he pulls a fast one.'

'Pay him,' Hugo told the bookkeeper.

'For *what?*' said Hy.

'He had 'em up on their feet. These bouts are the same – a musclehead pounding a numbnuts. I want heroes cliffhangers battle royals.'

The bookkeeper tore a CDP contract from a pad. I signed on the dotted line and he tore off a check for $289 made out to cash. Coming in Cully blocked the door.

'You paid *him?*'

'Any business of yours who gets paid?' Hugo asked him.

He moved aside and I went out to my pony and drove to the pool hall in wonder at having crossed paths with a fine individual like Hugo. Wrapped in Granme's quilt out back I counted my blessings. Making $120 a week for six days at the food bank and $100 for five at the dog patch, along with dock pay, I'd accumulated $500. The Channel 4 check made it $800. Pulling another stunt next Saturday night I'd be walking around with $1300. Yet to what end? I didn't want to run the deck slamming my hands on the mat and Hugo paying me out of embarrassment. I wanted to raise high shrieks.

Monday through Thursday afternoons I got work at the rail docks to bulge my old billfold all the more. Having run out on a bank debt in Louisville I didn't want to start a new account making known my whereabouts, so I went to a knife store and bought an expensive hand-tooled wallet with zipper, stuffing cash and checks inside.

Saturday noon I drove to an optical company on Cermak. Hornrims long out of style, I searched a box of donations and found a scratched pair that made my eyes cross. I paid $10 for plain lenses in hope marquees might hesitate to punch or choke a man wearing glasses.

I was unable think of anything new for Saturday night. If a marquee allowed it I could have come up with something for both of us but you can't be on equal terms with a narcissist. They hold in contempt any and all not as big and strong.

When I got to the armory, a guard was at the door, a retired political hack picking up side money, like they all do in Chicago.

'What's your business?'

'I'm on the wrestling show.'

He didn't believe it, just as quickly thumbing me in.

Jobbers arrived talking of being recognized by strangers. Hy came out gladhanding marquees and fawning kafabes, but Hugo remained in the office with his bookkeeper. I saw it as tactic. Going out to them would give them ego for the *Saturday Night Showdown* negotiations. Cold-shouldering them he gave nothing to go on. He knew he was dealing with swine and as the old Creole old Jew old Italian old Pole old *anybody* ever said, 'Show a pig a finger, he wants your whole hand.'

Marquees were so blasé about gift certificates kafabes handed out some were put on top of the lockers. I went ringside watching the arena fill up. Twenty-year-old loudmouths had me to start with. *'Run Punk Run!'* grew. Jackanapes and Up'n'Up Barry climbed into the ring. Cully came and found me.

'See Hy.'

I went to the rear where he had Yukon.

'Be his Svengali, put him through his paces, make him do your bidding, fight your battles, take blows meant for you. Then turn on him because you are the lowest of the low, one who turns on a friend. I see you as . . . *Gizmo!*'

He shook my arm like one does his member finishing masturbation. *'Show me Gizmo! Capture him!'*

167

I put on the hornrims and marched Yukon out to the camera eye. Climbing through the ropes I sensed this character I'd been put up to. Checking his card Terry Donley asked my name there.

'Gizmo.'

'Your purpose?'

'Svengali to Yukon Kid.'

Come down the ramp L'l All-America vaulted over the top rope. Bouncing to cheers he fixed an eye on me. There was a limit on how much he could pound a jobber, all of whom were bigger. Getting his hands on me he could maul me to his heart's content. Who would stop him, not the referee? The bell rang and Terry Donley called the match-up.

'In red corner from the North Woods at 266 pounds, Yukon Kid! Calling the shots, his Svengali Gizmo.'

'Small-time! Small-time! Pipsqueak!' came down on me as I turned roundabout.

'In blue corner at 200 pounds, the Cowlick Cyclone, Chicago's sawn-off Texan, L'l All-America!'

At the bell Yukon lunged and L'l America danced, but they didn't go, one too stiff the other too nifty. The same two weeks before, rabble soon tired of it. Slamming my hands on the mat to get Yukon to get his hands on him, I was taken ahold of and led to a utility room. Handed a thick wax bucket marked with skull and crossbones I followed Hy to the mop basin.

'Fill it cold, let 'em have it. Wake 'em up! *Sons a bitches* are killing me!'

'L'l All-America has it in for me. He gets his hands on me, who'll stop him?'

His face shot aflame. 'You *won't?*'

'Is there anything else I can do?'

'*Get out!*' he spat my face. '*Get out!* You don't sniff your own nuts around here, pal. Do what's called for. Now's first! *Now! Now!* Two minutes from now don't count a goddam. I give less than a *shit* for two minutes from now.'

Vibrating me with his hairy paw, he clamped the bucket into my hand.

'Show you got a pair! What am I paying you for?'

A full bucket I lugged along the corridor and down the ramp to wild hoots. Yukon had L'l All-America in a bear hug turning him under the lights. Red in the gills L'l All-America flailed like a baboon caught by a honey bear. Slapped round and round Yukon let go of him and L'l All-America swung onto his back.

Crouched aside the stoop I eyed L'l All-America across the ring bucking on Yukon's back and saluting the rabble. Turning him by his ruff he heeled his sides ignoring wild screams he was riding into a trap. At the thunder of Yukon's boots I rushed up the stoop splashing my pants and shoes. Heaved ho, the bucket lassoed my wrist. Cold water does not spray like hot. In a flume it cleared Yukon's head, splashing L'l All-America's mug. I fled emptyhanded, not wanting a look behind me. Crawling under the stands could not save me now, nor escaping to the rear where I would get no help. Loping up to the corridor I made for an emergency exit behind crates of Army reserve. The door not completely shut behind me I heard him coming.

'*Punk*, out here *punk!*'

Hy Speed was with him. 'He's a piece of crap. Why are you so mad?'

'I'll put him on a wheelchair. His ass is mine, Hy, hear?'

'Get back. Finish the match, goddam you!'

I stayed out until he finished with Yukon. From behind a crate I watched him come upramp and turn to the rear. I could stay hidden no longer. Earning my pay I wanted back at it. Hijinks and the ringside camera eye had left me intoxicated. Returned to impotent jeers and howls, in no fear of them now, I went up in the ring with jobbers even though they would not join with me, YMCA Kid even pinching his nose. Demanding the mic I insisted on being introduced as *Gizmo*, then ran the deck pounding the mat for no good reason. Jobbers taking their beatings and left prostrate, I stood over them. '*Why* don't you listen?' I whined for one and all. 'How *many* times . . .?'

Cocking my right heel over their heads brought Red Canyon to his feet.

'Dirty little coward! How dare you?'

Baboons pelted me with candy and balled up cups with pennies until I fled. At 'Y'all come again!' they began to vacate. Waiting until vendors packed up I went to the rear. Wrestlers had cleared out with their checks. Hy Speed counting the take, Hugo's assistant tore off a check for $289. I turned to go.

'You're not paying?' Hugo asked Hy.

'You paid. It's not enough for him?'

'He takes injury he's a guest.'

'I let him in he reciprocates, I'll fill you in on carny usage.'

'I'll peel your carny usage like an onion. Channel 4 doesn't contract with people who won't pay employees.'

Hy slapped down two tens a five.

In Hugo's eyes I stepped up on the bench by the marquees' lockers and retrieved two gift certificates to Shrimp Grill.

Arriving at Unity Sunday morning with $1300 in cash and checks, no sooner was I out of my pony when congregants came to ask if it was me on the Channel 4 wrestling show. Inside, my choir mates asked was it truly *me* with DiJi looking on. At the pulpit Reverend Brown veered off to modern entertainment, an arm out to all.

'I understand we have with us a young lion of television entertainment. Daupin, tell us what you were doing last night on the wrestling show on Channel 4?'

I answered proudly in his tone. 'I play a meddlesome scamp who likes to disturb combatants, make trouble, then git while the gittin's good.'

All there laughed, including DiJi.

'Be that your role, Daupin, as Martin Luther King said, play it well.'

Out back for refreshments DiJi looked accessible and I brought her ginger ale.

'Why didn't you tell anyone you were on TV?'

'It's only a testing for a possible weekly show.'

'They pay for that?'

My unzipped wallet revealed checks among thick cash.

'You must be good,' she blushed.

'I see no use doing anything if I can't do it good, add a little something personal – pride so to speak.'

Bertha the organ player came out to say song practice was cancelled.

'It's so early,' DiJi cried. 'I don't want to go home.'

'Would you prefer a Sunday ride?'

Borrowing a kerchief to wrap around her hair she got into the pony shifting her legs for room.

'Cozy,' she said.

My scrotum swelling twice over I turned the key. She put her hand over mine. 'Could we go to Bob's Inn?'

It was not like it sounded. Bob's was a place for respectable Negroes to go on weekends to socialize over good food and drink. Weekdays lawyers and judges worked out deals there. Afternoons women schoolteachers arrived in groups to cool their heels. Even at the pool hall, a hive of epithet speak, I heard respectful talk of Bob's Inn, hardly as whites usually talk about Negro establishments. I had desired to see it, now with DiJi we were on our way.

I lowered an eye at my billowed trousers, yet the fine weave made it seem not what it looked like. Expensive material will do that as cheap material will show you up. I turned into Bob's circling the wheel. Jacket folded over I gave DiJi the way. A doorman greeted us smartly. The hostess showed us to booth with good view.

DiJi for a gin fizz, I was for a Tom Collins, having oft heard the name, wanting to experience the taste. Giving DiJi some background omitting the humiliations and privations, in turn she said she came from downstate to care for her uncle who passed on. Taking a job as secretary and fundraiser for Reverend Brown she came in to take care of small matters then make calls to local companies for donations. She said her auntie was stingy and wanted too much of her for sleeping there. She might as well have waved the white flag.

I paid with a twenty getting back $16. Her drink ruby like her lips and nails, mine tall silvery with a cherry, a taste thrilled, Bob's drinks known to be strong. DiJi said again she wanted to move from her aunt's. I could not speak to her situation for no place of my own. Six nights a week I slept on cardboard flats and on Saturday night after the show I turned in behind the pool hall or under trees in front of Emil's.

'Have you married?' she asked.

'I was married almost three months.'

I sensed her notion I had taken a wife but was physically deficient to keep her fulfilled. Truth opposite of course, proof under a fold of my trousers, resting a hand there she would have instantly been relieved of her pity.

'What broke you up?' she posed.

'Co-workers came first, me last.'

'That's not how to treat a man. Do you think of her?'

'I do, yet as I sit with you she is far from mind.'

'Where did you live?' she blushed.

'Louisville, in a trailer.'

She let a whoop. 'A trailer is like playing house before you get one. You get tired of the scenery you move on.'

I wanted to suggest we start in one together, when two darkskin men strode by, her eyes following.

'Is wrestling all you do?' she asked.

'Goodness, no! I am nightwatchman at a food bank. Morns I work at a dog patch a quarter mile away.'

'What do you do there?'

'I care for sporting dogs.'

'A steady hardworking man, aren't you?'

'Thoughtful steady work begets much that is good.' I used Reverend Brown's tone.

'When you first pulled up,' she giggled, 'I saw a slick character looking to get over.'

'Nothing wrong with getting over if it's of honest effort.'

'Good for you because since I been here all I see is folks trying to get out of work, doing least they can, taking pride thereof. Downstate, only way they talk about a man is how hard he work. He known by that, no matter how he dress, long as somebody say, "There go a hardworker, sho nuf."'

She laughed at her imitation.

'Hardworkers should be respected everywhere. They're counted on to start the morn then make sure the day won't stall.'

'You speak so proper. You're not at all what you look like, Daupin.'

'I wear a slick suit but believe a man puts himself second to his duties. If he has family they come first and get all they need – he gladly settles for scraps if that's all that's left.'

She cozied up with her ruby lips. 'What do you see for yourself? You gonna be a TV show man?'

'Not necessarily in wrestling, I would like to do the news game.'

'*News!*'

173

'Yes, I've done much reading: ergo self-education, with little yen for the fanciful. I like facts and usually facts alone. I also think of myself as an enterpriser. Oft I think of how to make money. For instance the patch keeps ten dogs on a quarter acre, bringing $1200 a month. What if a fellow enterprises to keep twenty thirty forty? One vicinity good for twenty – why not a second third fourth? See it adding up? Much as I enjoy going about things myself I will require good help.'

'You're fascinating, Daupin, do people tell you?'

'People usually don't take time to get to know me.'

She cocked her head, liquor on her breath. 'I would like to.'

Two older gentlemen across the room could not for the life of them turn their eyes from her legs.

'What you told me a few weeks ago, DiJi.'

'What did I tell you?'

'You have big body parts and need a man with big hands to handle them.'

'Did I say that?'

'What a small man has, DiJi, does not always meet the eye. He might have more of what it takes to please than a bigger man.'

'That so?' her lips smacked.

'Y'know, one of dark Africa's ironies is that the pygmy side to side with other tribesmen stands as proud or prouder.'

Her tongue pushed out a cheek. 'You sayin' a pygmy man has a bigger daddy than a Watusi?'

'If that's how you please to put it?'

She let out *humph!*

Peeking down over my nose what I saw resembled an idiot in a closet with a coat over his head. Granme raised me to be bold. In the only sexual reference I heard her make, she said a small man must be bold to get *his*. Raised against vulgarity – to shun and disdain it – I saw a moment when one can not choose one without the other. I lifted her lacquered fingers to my lap. Tapping upward they groped headmost, squeezing twice as though she did not think it real. Her breath warmed my cheek, '*My* oh my!'

'Would you put me to the test?' I breathed.

She did not say no.

Jacket over arm I went to the lobby and paid $14 for a key. Returned I escorted DiJi out front and up a staircase to 10. She went in ahead, taking in the decor.

'Just a jiff,' she bid on way to privy, slipping off her heels.

Boldness called forth, *'DiJi!'*

Her lips parted.

'Will you come out *au natural*, so I may see you all at once – behold you so to speak?'

'We'll see, *won't* we?'

Shedding blouse pants shoes I had not beheld myself all at once for Granme had kept only small mirror glass. Sideward to full-length reflection I stared like an appalled onlooker: '*Good Gawd!*'

Coming out in only her glasses her throat muscles bobbed at what stood before her.

'You *do* have a big daddy.'

Sore eyes took in slopes and flanks of such size strength that a small man would be bucked off – unequipped to the task so to speak. On my toes our lips met. She lifted each breast to my tongue. Suckling like a babe I patted about her loins. Underhanded she took hold of me and led me to bed. Turning on her back she spread her legs to inlet and fleece. The way in was not narrow. Up wafted fruity aroma to my nostrils.

I thought to go it slow like a church brother but she soon sank and heaved in swoops and sways. Chin tucked nostrils awhine eyes bulged I plumbed her depth until my organ lept its last. Hot-cheeked she arched up for more. I rolled over in blessed relief.

We did not tarry. Mrs. Nelson who drove DiJi to and fro sat under an oak with Reverend Brown, Mrs. Brown and others of the inner circle, watching us turn into the lot. I dared no more than to press Diji's hand to my lips.

Our coupling was all my thought until Friday when Phillip said he was going to Maine and that he considered me a dog man now and would give me first chance at buying the patch for $2000. I would get ten hovels, chains leashes collars, five cases of Vets two sacks of dry meal. Rent for the property $140, keeping ten dogs brought in over $1200 monthly April to November. In cold months I could make expenses storing motor homes and boats.

Dog boarding would be smarter in a city where I could operate year round. Of a notion, though, that the new owner would not keep me, how blessed I felt to pull up there early morn from the food bank and go about.

Saturday I drove out to Maxwell Street, the once famous Jewish thoroughfare, where fine material unsold by original retailers could still be had – *sroyra* little Jewish tailors called it – if one had an eye to pick. A claret sharkskin within an hour was fixed in the cuffs, $90 in all. No wrestling show scheduled I spent the day at the pool hall.

Arriving at Unity Sunday morn I saw the same old camper in the lot, DiJi's mother and brother there again. She introduced me to them. Her brother was 'Theo'; her mother told me all called her 'Mammy.' Though I feared the day would be altered from expectation I sang head and shoulders above the others, the claret sharkskin so outstanding that Reverend Brown held back his head.

After prayers DiJi's mother and Theo took up positions at the curb and I felt required to invite them along. They followed in the camper to Bob's Inn. Well-to-do Negroes taking her eyes Mammy wanted them all to hear her go on about her stupid white neighbors, while Theo more than helped himself to short ribs and cornbread. Black people outeat white people. They have bigger appetites because they do not limit children's food as whites do especially in upper classes. Healthy appetites are taken in good humor but his running to the spread, cutting off others with his yellow eyes, snatching all he could made for grumbling.

Mammy and Theo did not get the idea to leave us be, sitting on as though I owed entertaining them further. Seeing DiJi and I would get no privacy I was disturbed by their presumptions until I got to the food bank that eve to start the week, silence and respite there for me as always. I had gone eight years between couplings, I could go yet another week.

Now that I wouldn't be in the eye of the Channel 4 camera I hoped to come eye to eye with a marquee, offering to let him get his hands on me if I could be sure of not being mauled. If at young age I could take being slammed to asphalt by rugged classmates I could take being manhandled by muscular buffoons – the charcoal sharkskin half gone anyway – but I suspected they would aim to cripple me. I was sure all of them had committed acts of pitiless theft, cowardly violence and sexual deviance. On those three I would have wagered.

I took dybuk out of wraps, snapping it forward and backhanding it like I once practiced. Should L'l All-America or another villain want to wring my neck and leave me an invalid, first I would stripe his face. He was not so much taller that I that could not inflict sharp cuts to that wild mug of his. I practiced encouraged by how old schoolmates at Jefferson spoke of Saturday matinee hero Lash Larue horsewhipping villains crooked bankers ugly saddle tramps when talk was useless.

Easy money is a hard taste to get out of your mouth, maybe hardest of all. Saturday night without Hugo and the protective eye of the Channel 4 camera, paid just $25 to

177

jeopardize myself with sadists, gave a lost feeling but I would go on not to miss out on a televised Saturday show.

A seamstress on Cermak sewed a catch into the lining of the charcoal sharkskin. Arrived to the armory with dybuk concealed I did not shirk from L'l All-America's eyes and this gave him pause as it would to any self-loving bucko.

Yukon first call I led him up through the ropes. A rough customer, Bullseye, up from Southern venues where face slaps were routine, playing a motorcycle hoodlum like Jackanapes but sounding genuine speaking the Nazi ideal of extermination of the weak and lame, came into the ring with the Iron Cross on back of a leather vest and a hemp noose tatooed between his shoulder blades. Hexagonal from overdeveloped thighs shoulders he slapped Yukon raw, going so slaphappy I could not distract him. Retreaing to the rear Yukon hung his head.

Going in with jobbers I insisted I be introduced first, then exhorted them against marquees, running the deck and waving them on. By now I knew what marquees I could harass, cracking dybuk at their heels. After jobbers received their beatings and lay prostrate I waited until marquees tramped away, re-entered the ring and cracked down on them with dybuk until their limbs jerked and howls went up. *Damn your hide! Damn you to hell!* Up on his feet came Red Canyon red with rage. Baboons throwing what they could I fled under the bottom rope.

I stood last in line to be paid, jobbers ahead already doubting Channel 4 would be back. Waxing his cowlick L'l All-America told a marquee he would get me. I didn't hear it but his lips said so. Taking $25 I wheeled across the lot toward the corner of 51st and saw Yukon alone on a bus bench. A carload of louts sweeping through the intersection shouting satanic chants splatterd him with a water balloon. Jumping up he looked down at himself. A follow-up car went by to let him have it again and he did something I hardly

178

believed I saw. Getting a heel up on the bench he sprang backwards over the backrest. I pulled up behind him and he swung around as though being attacked again.

'C'mon.'

I drove to a counter and he finished a hamburger like one polishes off a cupcake, then sat back as if it was enough. He did not look up at the wall menu or at anything anyone else had.

I stared at skin nearly broken at his eyes.

'Why do you do this? You could get a truck and go out in the world.'

'I quit school when I was twelve. I don't have formal training.'

I could have said the same.

'You went to work?'

'My mother laid out with emphysema lit up a smoke and fire shot into her lungs. They took her out her face burned black. I was six-two in fifth grade, anyway. I got out on the road for myself.'

'Where was this?'

'Yukon Territory.'

'You lived off the land?'

'I asked at roadhouses and groceries what they had to throw out then found a place where I could lay my head daytime and moved on after dark. You'd think it'd be the other way but that's how you keep going. People got it in for an overgrown boy out on his own.'

He spoke more than I thought he would but looked past me.

'How long did you go like that?'

'Six months. I came to a timber camp. Chinese woman in the kitchen said if I cleaned up after her she'd feed me.'

'You learned to be a lumberjack?'

'I was climbin' cuttin' when I was fourteen.'

'Lumberjacks looked out for you?'

'I turned fifteen they took me out, got me drunk and beat the shit out of me. I was laid up in a house two weeks.'

I understood why he was aloof.

'How long were you at it?'

'Eleven years camp to camp up into Alaska.'

'You quit for this?'

'I went out on the road to visit my father.'

'Where was he may I ask?'

'Barber shop Fort Knox, Kentucky. I thought he'd put me up, we'd get to know one another, but he had two boys. Not much more he could do but sit awhile over a cigarette. I didn't want to go back to timber so I took to wrestling.'

'You didn't consider sports, the size of you? Nobody came and got you?'

'I played summer football in Alaska when I was sixteen, $50 a game, like I get here.'

'You couldn't follow up?'

'The league quit.'

'Why wrestling?'

'It was on Saturday nights. We used to tussle in the bunkhouse.'

'You knew it was fake?'

'Tell me what ain't whole or part, just the inscription put over you when you die – if that's true. I saw enough of what's real.'

'You plan to make a go of it?'

'If I can go national, Hy don't pay much.'

'I heard you're on the road for years.'

'I did it on foot I can do it in a car. I don't like getting familiar.'

'You have anything else going?'

'What do you mean?'

'Work?'

'I don't have a work number. I don't need much. I get food behind the market. A guy and me snag empties scrap.'

180

Seemed to me he had insufficient belief in himself. I looked at his swollen face.

'You jumped over a bench backwards. You could be light on your feet. You don't have to flatfoot like Frankenstein and take beatings.'

'I don't know what I'm doin'. I don't wanna get too free with myself.'

'You don't want anybody mad at you?'

'I spent $3000 for school.'

'*Three thousand!* What did you learn? You could have taught yourself from television.'

'I got training to get through doors.'

He'd been fed that line. He was uneasy with me strong on him. I got to business.

'You and I team now. I would like to count on you. Those marquees get their hands on me I will be in a bad way. I can only look to you, and don't say you can't do anything. You could break any of them in two. I say join up, look out for one another.'

I drove to a sagging woodframe that stood long years. Lights had a right to be off but I sensed nobody lived there. Pulling away I eyed an old school bus in back, with a notion it was where he slept.

Pulling up in front of Emil's I wrapped myself in Granme's quilt. Monday DiJi was leaving with Mrs. Nelson and her two sisters on a tour through Kentucky Tennessee, but morrow I would take her to Bob's Inn to again lay eyes on her *au natural*. Getting to the pool hall at daybreak I changed to the claret sharkskin, sat over coffee and drove to Unity.

Mammy and Theo were out front with a 'Here we are look.' I could not hide my displeasure even as I sang. DiJi and I making our way out, they were at the curb, noses pointed in the direction of Bob's Inn, following us there. Hardly in her seat she started again about everyone calling her 'Mammy', wanting black matrons to take up with her while Theo with his orange head and yellow eyes all but ran to the spread to snatch up chicken dumplings. Silently I suffered this curse that came with DiJi. Out front for a stroll I let her know I was offered the dog patch for $2000.

'*Will* you take it?'

'Dog keep will be my future, DiJi, if television opportunity won't arise, but it's only a seven-month business here. I would start in a warmer place.'

'Where?'

'Does Florida sound good?'

'Florida!'

'Keep Japan in mind.'

'*Japan!* What have you in mind there, Daupin?'

'Please allow a secret for now.'

Saturday night Yukon was matched against Jackanapes again and despite my antics to interfere took a beating. At times jobbers looked ready to turn and fight but marquees saw none of this from him, letting him have it all they wanted to. He got beatings because they did not want to grapple with him. He was too rangy to manhandle, boned so large that when they meant to swing him into a corner they were lifted off their feet. I had seen big-boned Negroes in Louisville but never of Yukon's length and width both. As marquees 'overpowered' him it was obvious to anyone over five years old he went along, his face unchanged throughout.

Hy Speed grabbed him in the corridor. 'Show some feeling. You cigar store Indian, you oaf, you totem pole, what are you doing to me?'

He would have let him go but it wasn't easy to keep feeding jobbers to marquees. Two had already quit. Yukon and I said little to one another. It was obvious he shamed to join with me – whether it was rascal Gizmo or my color size limp.

Watchful from early age I thought I saw all but not my own way, unsure what walk of life becomes an heir to a

182

throne – botany perhaps but it was out of my possibilities. Finally I saw opportunity in television or more likely dog keep, at which I was sure I could succeed from sheer will. What a competitor had over me in facility and staff I would make up in time and thought. One who likes to take care thinks two three four steps ahead. No venal foe can match that. He is left scratching his neck. Fine chance, possibly two, lay ahead but what turns one off good way to risk, holds the old Creole, comes in threes and three in three straight days defies coincidence.

Friday eve I sat awhile at the pool hall before going to the food bank to finish the week. Taped to the glass door was a newspaper article with photo of a heavyset man I oft saw there kidding around with DPs. Nearly all bald over the thickest roundest rosiest neck I ever saw he wore sporty shirts and shoes for his age and had a jaunty step. I guessed he'd been successful and still had a thing or two going.

Cabe Nebo he was, National Football League offensive lineman through the early 50s to early 60s, one of few foreign born players in its history. Retired two decades he kept a hand in the game by scouting small college football for a *find,* an unknown who played like a man among boys. He had great memories of a decade in the NFL, regretting only being paid peanuts and missing out on salaries paid today's lineman. Modern pay did not seem real to him. He did not make in his entire career the first-year minimum now, $155,000. Finishing the article I thought little more of it.

Saturday, Memorial Day weekend, was the last show until July. National Guard took over the armory the month of June. Hy Speed brought in Roger Plath the Pro, 260-pound lineman for the Chicago Bears who wrestled off-season. Usually working televised venues, his game was to leave a man wobbly against the ropes, then charge across the ring with a flying shoulder block, ramming home the win. A handsome substantial man, he charged Yukon that night but it was not Yukon who shook. Watching Roger bounce like a boy at play with an adult I formed a notion that came whole next morn at Unity.

A man six-three arrived in a lime green suit and alligator shoes. At the close of service he was introduced as former football player Jackson Forte. Called to the pulpit he said he had played in the National Football League nine years, seven with the Houston Oilers two with the San Diego Chargers, signing for a $50,000 bonus, making Pro Bowl twice and earning a half million dollars. Little to show for it he kept bar at 41st and Ashland with a billy under the counter. In his case it was not the usual suspects: strong stimulants fast women large autos – but foppery. He had seduced himself into grandiosity, becoming a popinjay of outlandish coats and vests to go with fedoras and shoes so bizarre they outdid many a clown's. It was no more he admitted than a need of a poor Mississippi boy to show his *a-s-s* to the world and that he made of himself. At not a tremor from him in front of complete strangers I wondered did he really felt regret or was he one of those Negroes whose voice does not break, even facing a noose? At that very moment, my head came as clear as in boyhood, just as clear to me opportunity Granme foretold.

Confessed he greeted all outside with a tidy white bible. I introduced myself.

'Daupin Capet, I took your words to heart.'

He shook my hand, giving my claret sharkskin a look.

'Thank you, brother.'

'Watching football a few years now I have a question.'

'Shoot.'

'I work on the wrestling show at the Armory as the character Gizmo. I team up with a raw wonder who goes by Yukon Kid, six foot six, 266 pounds, startling to lay eyes on. Last night we wrestled Roger Plath the Pro from the Chicago Bears.'

'He's wrestling off-season?'

'If you can call it that? Charging into Yukon he bounced like a boy. What I would ask, if this Yukon can turn back an NFL player can he be there himself?'

Jackson laughed, 'Woa, Woa, awhole lot more to being in the league than that.'

'If you saw how he toyed with this Roger fellow it might make you wonder. He can jump backward over a bus bench.'

'You tellin' tales now,' he blushed.

'He was hit by a water balloon at a corner; a second car came by to splash him again and he tapped a heel on the bench and jumped the backrest.'

'Clear over?'

'To the other side and landed on his feet.'

'How old is he?'

'Twenty-six. You're a man who saw action. I am but an onlooker, but I see a defensive charger in him.'

'He played football?' Jackson asked.

'Semi-pro in Alaska when he was sixteen.'

'He didn't play college?'

'He hardly went to school.'

'He needs college – college somewhere.'

'It can't be done without college?'

'It's been done. Cats off the street, a few out of high school even. It don't happen now. The game's too specialized.'

'But it happened?'

He nodded.

'Were they effective?'

'Some.'

'Yukon would be one. Would you have a look at him?'

'I'd have to go with him in pads. He's 26, he don't have much time.'

'If I arrange it you'd meet him?'

185

'I still like to mix it up. It don't leave the blood. I got the Oiler helmet and Pro Bowl. Get him shoulder pads, I'll go with him. I can't do it free.'

'What would you ask?'

'Fifty, I can use new sneakers.'

'How long would it take to see if he has anything?'

'A few whaps, his fight come out or don't – he get a snootful, he still wanna stick it in there. It's called *game* like in a rooster – see if he got game or he just another stiff which most of 'em is.'

'You can't hold him off, it means he has what it takes?'

'I'm gon' hold him off, no question. I didn't go Pro Bowl two years on nuthin'!'

'Let's respectfully say you can't, he has something?'

'I can't, he got sumthin' alright. I'll give you my number.'

Monday, Memorial Day, I finished at the patch, drove to 61st, went up the porch of the old woodframe and knocked to nothing. The schoolbus open round back I went up the stoop. All but front seats gone, Yukon was on a mattress in back. I called him out.

'I know Jackson Forte who played for the Houston Oilers and San Diego Chargers. I told him how Roger Plath bounced off you Saturday night and how you jumped backward over a bus bench. He said he will take a look at you.'

'For what? I didn't play college, how can I go pro?'

'Not all NFL players went to college. Some came off the street. He wants to go against you in pads. If Roger Plath plays professional football so can you.'

'He went to school and got trained.'

'He bounced off you, he was helpless. How could he stand against you on the field? He's paid thousands of dollars to put on a uniform.'

'Football is something else.'

'You said you played.'

'Oil companies started up a league one summer.'

'How did you do?'

'I stood my ground.'

'You couldn't go elsewhere?'

'Where? I never saw a city till I was twenty.'

'Salary for a first year man is $155,000. You make $50 a match with Hy. Will you challenge yourself?'

'How do I get on?'

'I know of an NFL scout at a pool hall who looks for unknowns. You show Jackson something, I will ask him to come see you.'

I found a pay phone and looked up Sporting Goods in the *Yellowbook*. A wholesaler said he had pads to fit a 260-pound man. I drove to a dive near downtown. He swung them up on a dingy counter and took $45.

Returned to 61st I didn't find Yukon in the bus. He could not be far away it seemed. Ten minutes on he and a bum crossed the intersection pushing a buggy of bottles. Getting his head through the pads he settled them on his shoulders.

'I'll go against him,' he breathed, 'who's gonna want me?'

'You can turn back other men you'll be wanted. I'll come get you to meet Jackson Forte.'

'He's not lookin' for trouble is he? He's not gonna want to start somthin'?'

'He was a professional player. He only wants to see what you can do.'

I returned to the pay phone and called Jackson at his work. 'I have shoulder pads. Yukon says he'll go against you?'

'It's got to be early. I'm here noon six days a week.'

'I work at a dog patch mornings Monday through Friday.'

'Make it Saturday, nine or so at the park off 42nd.'

187

Saturday daybreak I left the food bank and drove to the pool hall for coffee. Cabe Nebo came in at seven. I held off, things were not in line yet. At 8:30 I drove out to 61st, stepping around the bum on the bus stoop. Yukon was in back.

'He wants to see you.'

He put on his boots and we drove east to a small park with a grass bank. Jackson in football cleats and shoulder pads stood aside a yellow Seville, good to his word. I presented my charge to him.

'Yukon, eh, that your real name?'

'I've been going by it,' he said hanging back.

'You look a stud alright,' Jackson gave him. 'It used to count for sumthin' but everybody gotta be able to dig out their own bones now. Let's see what you got.'

I got out the pads, not a recent make. Yukon pulled them over his head. Jackson tied the laces, tugged a light-blue jersey down over Yukon's shoulders and handed him a white Oiler helmet he barely pulled down over his ears.

Jackson took off his glasses and I helped him pull his jersey over his pads. Putting on his gold Pro Bowl helmet he and Yukon went down the bank to flat ground.

'Show me a stance.'

Yukon squatted in a position that looked awkward to me.

'Come straight, don't sideswipe me.'

Yukon lunged clapping his hands against Jackson's pads. Jackson nodded. They squared off and Yukon sprang, bending him back.

'Come harder,' said Jackson, 'drive your legs.'

Yukon swung out turning him in a curve.

'Chin tucked in, head straight,' Jackson said. 'Turn your chin in the NFL you'll get hit so hard you'll think it was Rocky Marciano.'

Yukon unwound and Jackson brought his fists up under his chin snapping back his head. Yukon wheeled him around until Jackson threw loose.

'Take the lick on the point of the chin. Don't turn your jaw and give 'em a way to knock you out.'

Getting the idea Yukon had him backpeddaling. I thought Jackson was going along but started to see Yukon too strong on him. His legs giving, unable to plant a foot, he was nearly run down. Cleaning his cleats he waved me over.

'Stand there like a quarterback, we'll go one for keeps.'

I got twenty feet behind him.

'Get to Gizmo,' he told Yukon, bulling his neck.

I crouched. *'Set! Go!'*

At a clap of pads Jackson had him squared off. A chortle rose in his throat. One heel lifted and the other lost hold. Scampering back out of control he bounced on his back to me. I jumped aside and caught hold of Yukon's arm.

'Take off the helmet, walk around and cool off.'

Jackson pulled himself up.

'You told no lie,' he breathed going back down on a knee. 'He's raw but you told no lie.'

'You're not in condition, maybe?'

'My timin's off but he's like you say. Everywhere you go you hear about some natural waitin' his chance but this guy is strong.'

'You think pro teams will look at him?'

'They'll look.'

'Can he make a team?'

'He can bullrush but can he turn a corner? Does he have a nose for the ball? Does he even want to be a pro because if he's not sure he won't be nuthin'?'

He thought aloud. 'It's June. I work with him three times a week, get him up to twenty a day, show him things they teach you in college, he'll go to camp in July like he's been schooled. I got the time, I can't do it on promise. I'm risking what's left of my knees. It'll get heavy. I have to get paid.'

'How much?'

'Fifty a time.'

Recalling Granme's admonition I took $50 from my wallet.

'What are you expecting out of this?' he asked.

'I'll take twenty percent of his first contract and handle odds ends if he wants me to.'

'Usually it's five, no more than ten.'

'I saw this for him, he makes $50 a week wrestling. Out of $155,000 he'll have plenty.'

'He don't get it all at once; he taxis it don't come to a third.'

'How do they pay?'

'The showers after games. You trust him to go to the bank Monday morning and send your share?'

'I'll have to.'

I waved Yukon over, his eyes not so distant now. The clash did him good.

'Jackson says he can get you ready to go to an NFL camp in July. It depends on if you will train?'

'I'll train.'

'Jackson is witness. I will pay him to work with you three times a week. For the money I put into this I want twenty percent of your contract. It's a lot but you'll keep four times more.'

I helped him pull off his jersey and pads, handing them and the Oiler helmet to Jackson. Sessions were arranged for Monday Wednesday and Saturday instead of Friday so I could be there once a week. The park four miles from Yukon, I drove him back, stopping at a currency exchange, cashing the checks and changing cash to fifties. Buying a roll of tokens for him I drove him to the corner where he would get on a bus three times a week to go meet Jackson.

I was in for $150 a week. Seven times that half through July came to $1000 on the line for a payoff. My self-perception from pauper to sportsman, there's a feeling you get just pulling on your pants knowing yourself that.

I did not go to Unity Sunday in fear of Mammy and Theo showing up even without DiJi there. Day whiled away at the pool hall I got a red hot before driving to the food bank to start the week.

Monday morn two sportsmen came for their dogs leaving eight. They said not a word to me. Part Negro and no sportsman I wondered if such men would trust their dogs to me without Phillip present. More on my mind I sped down Adams Road to a pay phone to call Jackson at work.

'Jackson, Daupin, how did it go?'

'He came late.'

'You trained?'

'I had him comin' round left.'

'Did he get by you?'

'He stands you still with those red hands and swings himself around. I seen light linebackers do it on a blitz, nobody his size.'

'You couldn't hold him off?'

'I rode him out a few times but he was turnin' the corner, and left's not his strong side.'

'You like what you saw?'

'He was still late.'

'He doesn't work. An opportunity like this he should be on time.'

I thought to go to Yukon to ask why, but to support money going out I drove to the rail docks, getting three days straight.

Finished at the patch Wednesday I drove to the pay phone.

'How did it go?'

191

'I had him comin' right. He turns you out and cuts across your inside shoulder like an engine switching tracks.'

'Was he late?'

'Fifty minutes.'

'He's not late for wrestling.'

'He don't believe in this you trust him to cut you a share? I seen his type. They get all they can out of you and leave you hangin' out to dry, forget they knew you. I'd get him to sign a contract and have it looked at.'

I got a wallet calendar at a liquor store and crossed off June 6th 7th 8th 9th 10th.

Early Saturday I took the call at the food bank, washed up and put on the charcoal sharkskin and hornrims. No idolator – far from it – I believed in one God only and put stock no false idols, but Gizmo was getting the better of me, his manner more than mine to get me through this. Taking my pay I drove to the pool hall, sat over coffee, then drove to 61st in a drizzle, going to the abandoned bus and stepping around the bum on the stoop. He did not look old despite gray whiskers and gave a dirty look for nothing better to do. Yukon sat on the mattress in back, turned to a window, picking at his groin, rolling a louse between thumb and forefinger.

'What are you doing to yourself?'

'I got crabs from the mattress.'

I thought a moment. 'Let's skip today and find you a room to sleep.'

Good to his word Jackson was at the park. I rolled down the window in the drizzle.

'He has crotch lice. He sleeps on a bus with a bum. I have to find him a place.'

Pinching three fifties out of my wallet I paid him.

'Get Z-1 at the drugstore,' he said. 'Tell him to rub it in and wash it out in the morning.'

Looking relieved he wouldn't go against Yukon, he said he would be there Monday. I went to a drugstore and found the ointment on the shelf without having to ask. On the way out I picked up the *Green Sheet* and looked for rooms, finding an address out on 74th by the city line. Returned to Yukon out on the bus stoop I handed him the tube.

'Go rub this between your legs and wash it out morrow morn.'

Spreading the *Green Sheet* across the passenger seat I drove him west to a steeple house on a gravel lot, met by an uncombed head behind a screen door.

'One not two.'

'He not me,' I answered in kind. Gizmo had my tongue. He stepped out in ragged bathrobe, looking at Yukon like he had never seen such a person. His wife stared out.

'Does he work?' he asked.

'He's a wrestler, he trains, that's his work.'

'I want employed renters.'

'He's a *giant*, I'm afraid!' the wife called out.

We went to a hovel on stone floor five feet wide eight deep. With bunk came blanket pillow and string to a light bulb overhead. Excusing himself to Yukon he beckoned me out.

'What kind of person is this big? It is not normal.'

'He is quiet and used to being alone. He will not bother you.'

Picking at his lips he wanted a month's rent and $30 security.

I showed Yukon the corner to catch a bus to the park. He asked if I would take him somewhere to eat. I drove him to Dag's # 9 for the jackpot breakfast, three eggs potatoes toast for $1.25. For its large servings Dag's starting at one place now numbered fourteen. I sat with tea.

'Once you rid yourself of your pests we will throw out the mattress there and bring a new one. You were late Monday and Wednesday. On a good night's sleep you'll be on

193

time. Has it sunk in you will be in camp with a team late July?'

'How do I get there?'

'I told you. When Jackson has you ready I will ask the scout at the pool hall to come see you in action. You are the type he looks for – someone nobody else knows.'

Getting his rucksack from the bus I drove him back to the room, dazed by what I'd gotten myself into, $175 a week going into Yukon's training, money that but days ago was like lifeblood to me.

I drove to the pool hall. Cabe Nebo wandered in among DPs. Keeping an eye on him I followed him out.

'Mr. Nebo.'

'I *know* you?'

I didn't take it as unfriendly, he might have a hard time keeping people straight.

'I work on the wrestling show at the armory as the character Gizmo. I read the newspaper story taped to the door. You travel through the Midwest scouting football players, do you?

'Not like I used to.'

I work with a wrestler Yukon Kid, over six foot six, 266 pounds, a rawbone wonder, a lumberjack. He was not made at YMCA or in a garage. He is training with Jackson Forte who played for the Houston Oilers.'

'I remember Forte.'

'They put on helmets and go at it. Jackson says he can't hold him off.'

'Forte wasn't big in his day. He wouldn't make a tight end now.'

'He played nine years and made Pro Bowl twice. He says he's never seen anyone like Yukon.'

'How old is he?'

'Twenty six.'

'You mean 32 going on 26, sleepin' in a garage and wearing the same jeans every day?'

'He said 26.'

'What college did he play for?'

'He didn't go to a college; he grew up in timber camps and played in Alaska.'

'What is he, a big Indian?'

'White with red hair like Tarzan of the Apes.'

'Bring him.'

'Can we invite you to the park on 42nd to see him in action? If you have a business card I'll call.'

Reluctantly he went back in and jotted down his telephone number for me.

Monday morn Phillip told me he was leaving late June and asked if I wanted to take over. The sandblaster next door and his son wanted to take the patch but he would give me first chance. I didn't have the $2000.

'How much can you put down? I don't want you left out.'

I gave thought to what I would have in my wallet after Yukon shipped out.

'I could put down $500.'

'I'll tell the bank you're a good worker.'

I followed him into the trailer to booth and counter, one-burner stove, small sink and 'fridge', privy with shower, coin phone on the wall and sleep for two in back. Going about my work I thought it through. I would be cutting it thin between Yukon and the dog patch but if I didn't take over I would likely be out of the job and $100 a week. Getting occupancy back to ten dogs would bring in $1200 a month to November. I would experience income and outgo and gain smarts so that when I went to warmer climate to start anew I would not be easy to fool, like Hugo the Channel 4 co-ordinator did not let marquees and Hy Speed pull the wool over his eyes. Most of all I thrilled at the thought of telling DiJi on her return I had a trailer for us.

Two o'clock I drove to a phone to call Jackson.

'How did it go?'

'He came from both sides. I can't hold him off. I cut down on him a few times not to be so sure of himself. A raw cowboy like him is gonna get cut, but he bends a knee and skips around.'

Chancing further good news I asked if he was on time.

'He came late.'

'He say why?'

'I don't ask. We don't have long to go. It'll be on their hands when he signs.'

A loan officer arrived at the patch Wednesday morn. I had taken a liking to young men in white shirt and necktie who helped you out in tragedy and opportunity. We worked out $500 down $70 a month 36 months, besides $140 rent for the trailer and quarter acre. I took ten fifties out of my wallet and signed on the line to become a legitimate businessman.

Phillip and I spent noontime calling clients to introduce me as the new owner. Two sportsmen said they would come to get their dogs the day they were paid up to, which would leave me six. Taped to wall was a business license along with numbers of the fire department, veterinary clinic and feed store he did business with. Sitting me down he showed me how to record expenses and proceeds, which was easy enough. Finished there I drove to a phone. Jackson wasn't himself.

'I went at him. He got billets for arms. He shoots out those hands I couldn't go another step. The league's forty pounds heavier now but they won't get to him, either. He's too strong. They'll trap and turn him but they won't drive him.'

'Nobody will?'

'It'd take one ugly son of a bitch!'

196

I took out the calendar and crossed off 11th 12th 13th 14th 15$^{th.}$.

Thursday morn Phillip took down the hangar he worked under, piled canvas staves poles into a hitched trailer, loaded his personals and drove off.

DiJi was due back Sunday 19th. First two days I had sole responsibility the dogs would be left to themselves ten at night to daybreak. The area was light industry and their barking could attract a vagabond or miscreant. They were not the type to scare anybody off, not a biter among them. I could only rely on a little luck I had in cutting corners for it was scarce in most else.

Two sportsmen coming for their dogs were right about me were they not going by my color, sensing something unfit about my taking over. Done with the dogs by noon, little else to do I took out the calendar, a month or so to go until NFL camps opened. At 9:30 I fixed them dry meal with canned corn so they might not bark of hunger. Switching off the light over the trailer I left them in a sliver of moon. A lurcher attracted to the fence would not clearly see a barker unless he cast a beam.

At the end of their chains, chests out they cried for me to come back. Locking the gate behind me I drove to the food bank pulling up the ramp into the track. Workers gone I cleaned swept as usual then fixed myself a sandwich from the block of cheese. I could not entertain a *National Geographic* and lay down on cardboard flats unable to close my eyes, chiding myself for putting innocent animals at risk.

Getting the call earlier than usual I had not slept. I soaped up and rinsed off, then wiped down the pony. Laying back down I gave to slumber. Up before six I got behind the wheel, marking the minutes.

The gate rolled up. Getting the nod from the supervisor I bumped down the ramp into pale light and sped back the quarter mile, pulling uphill. On their hind legs I counted

197

seven. Billy the blind beagle was not out, his chain curled back. Running to I found him in his hovel stretching his forelegs. The tan retriever and gray pointer damp with dew, they had stood out all night waiting. I dried them off, cleaned the area and fed them all, sitting a blessed moment before taking them for a walk.

Noon I called Jackson at work to tell him I wouldn't be at the park Saturday morn. All of Friday on my hands, when I fixed the dogs a late snack they cried as they ate. They could not defend themselves against a poacher and they knew it.

Night going no faster I beat back forth in the center aisle. When the gate came up daybreak I doubted my sleep was worth two cents. I wheeled back the quarter mile, finding them all at the ends of their chains. I'd gotten away with it but was left mumbling to myself, something I had never done before.

Noon I called Jackson at the tavern.

'How did it go?'

'He didn't show . . . I waited over an hour.'

I couldn't speak a moment.

'He overslept?'

'I been smellin' sour beer on him, a smell all its own early. Can you get out to him?'

'Not for a few days . . . I'll call you Monday.'

A sportsman arrived for the gray pointer, his manner brusque without hello goodbye. A black man would not do that to a white man. By nature he meets strangers happily but I always suspected a white man is born cold and needs to be trained out of it. Yukon strong on me I felt some relief that DiJi would return morrow and I wouldn't leave the dogs that night.

Like I had been doing I fixed them a late snack and took Granme's quilt from the pony into the trailer. A clean mattress I laid down on, sleeping in my own bed the first time in eight years. Morn the dogs gave thanks I had not left them.

Noon I called to DiJi at her aunt's, told she was home with her mother. Getting the number there I put in five quarters and dialed downstate. DiJi answered in poor spirits.

'DiJi, why aren't you here? I have the dog patch and trailer.'

'You meant to go to Florida?'

'I can gain experience while I wait for Channel 4 to make up their minds, but I need you to move in.'

'Mammy strained her back. She hasn't even done spring cleaning yet.'

'Why does she need you, she has your brother?'

'He won't clean. He says it's women work.'

'*Women* work! When work is necessary, you do it.'

'He won't.'

'*Won't!* Don't feed him he'll turn into a cleaning fool. He'll dance with that mop.'

'He's pigheaded, no use discussing it. We tried. Next Sunday I'll bring my things.'

'One thing,' I cautioned, 'you will be sleeping alone. There are no neighbors. A plating business is to one side, a sandblaster on the other.'

'Just take me from my auntie. I was biting my thumbs not to talk back.'

'I'll get everything ready, DiJi.'

To next Sunday I would leave the dogs alone six more nights. Could I ask the food bank supervisor for a week off after being there only two months? I'm sure it would put my position at risk, but that wasn't my only problem.

I took a notion to hire a dog boy to come in three mornings a week while I brought Yukon to Jackson and made sure they went at it. DiJi had told me Reverend Brown knew how to work the system. Chicago Youth Authority sent him workers to help care for his mother-in-law in a wheelchair and it cost near nothing.

Taking the directory I found the Reverend's home number on Homestead Rd. It took a good few rings.

'Reverend Brown, Daupin here.'

'We missed you today, what is your mind?'

'Reverend Brown, I just bought a dog patch that has me tied up. I board seven and can use help.'

'Congratulations, Daupin. Up and coming entrepreneurs are one of our great hopes. Your timing is downright canny. CYA sends a boy to attend my wife's mother, Mrs. Turner. She leaves tomorrow for Memphis. I can get this young man transferred to you on personal reference. You have business license?'

'I do.'

'He's a sour plum but likes it he has a job.'

'He did well by your mother-in-law, Mrs. Turner?'

'My mother-in-law is not easy to please. The Twelve Apostles on three shifts would not quite do.'

'What age is the young man?'

'Twenty-four.'

'What did he do to be under CYA?'

'I looked over his jacket. Daddy blew by; mama left him with Southern Baptists when he was eight and lit out with a man. Those Baptists started pullin' down his pants and whippin' his ass while he yellin' "Help me, Jesus!" Scripture was at the center of all that insanity. Turnin' twenty he came up on a bus and got work at a schvitz, shaving old Jewish men's balls and mopping up the place. Losing faith he fell in with dandies at the bus station, gangin' up on streetwalkers and playin' look-out on handoffs. Police took him in. He gave a smart tone, caught some whacks and tried to drown himself in a toilet. A mental health officer came to investigate and he made statements that would commit a man – he was the illegal son of Red Skelton.'

'What's his name?'

'Clee, Clee Doss.'

200

Yes, I remembered his low character in Miss Pierre's class yet to this day cringed at the way Granme had treated his mother when he was a slippery little butterball of three years. He was the only relative I had left.

'Pay $5 for him weekdays, and you can hold him free two weekends a month, long as he gets three meals and his own room. We have him now. Take him to your dogs, see if he's who you're lookin' for.'

Reverend Brown's place was a mile down Homestead Road from the Unity, a woodframe with a long front of grass. The Reverend, the misses and mother-in-law sat outside. Coming across he brought me to Mrs. Brown and elderly Mrs. Turner in a wheelchair.

'Are you the young *gallant* sparkin' DiJi?' cheered Mrs. Brown.

'I plead guilty as charged,' I said. 'I was taken with DiJi the moment I saw her.'

'DiJi's been looking quite awhile. You came along not a day too soon.'

'Daupin bought a dog patch,' said Reverend Brown. 'He's here to see Clee.'

Mrs. Turner nearly rose out of her chair. 'He the enemy of all mankind. He bitter as gall. He friendless.'

Reverend Brown gave me a look.

'He's no blessing,' said Mrs. Brown, 'but he will do a job for you and cheap to keep. He'll keep a piece of gum all week and eat turkey butts, don't want nuthin' else.'

'He the enemy of all mankind,' hailed Mrs. Turner. 'His whole family in jail because of him.'

'Don't make a fuss over him,' said Mrs. Brown. 'Let him know who's in charge or he gets uppity.'

Reverend Brown brought out a sullen hollow-eyed boy, hardly taller than me.

'Clee, this gentleman has a business and needs help with his dogs. Care to see his animals?'

He mewled with his chin tucked in.

'Would you like to work with dogs?' I put to him.

His lips curled, meaning yes.

Putting the top down to give him a sense of freedom, I waved back to the Reverend, his misses and mother-in-law, swinging out on Homestead.

'Have you had a dog, Clee?'

'I had a chicken, somebody wrung its neck.'

'A dog is a noble animal, Clee. It will give its life, asking little in return. To call a bad person a dog is unfair to dogs.'

It made no impression on him.

'Do I look familiar, Clee?'

'I know you is.'

'Who?'

'You Gizmo, I seen you on television. You like to cut and run. Everybody in the hall say Gizmo ain't nuthin' but a punk.'

'Gizmo is a character I play, Clee. Gizmo is not the real me.'

I turned my head. 'You know the real me, Clee. Remember in Miss Pierre's class at Carver Elementary? I helped you with lessons.'

It slowly came.

'Oh *yeh*.'

'You have family, Clee?'

'I got a midget uncle. He smoke a cigar.'

'He does?'

'He drive a car. He don't like you he hit you in the privates. You bend over he sock you on the jaw.'

I sensed he wanted family so badly he made him up; I would not tell him yet we were cousins.

'When did you start working for Reverend Brown, Clee?'

'Summer last.'

202

'Must not be easy taking care of elderly.'

'Mrs. Turner hold it all mornin' then say, "Clee, I have to shit and piss; make fast." When I sleep Mrs. Brown come in and start pullin' on my privacy tool. She come one night butt nekked. I look away. She say, "Why, Clee, do you think a human body is nasty?" I say "Yo' body's nasty, Mrs. Brown."'

Pulling uphill I unlocked the gate and let each dog sniff him around as he looked down at them through slit eyes.

'Outside dogs, Clee, need little more than firm hand and timely care. No need to pamper them.'

I took him to the workbench, showing him cases of Vets and the dry meal.

'A working dog like a working man, Clee, loves cool clean water. Like to fill their bowls?'

He picked up water bowls and brought them to the hose.

'See to their water, Clee, that's a good part of it.'

I now laid out procedure. 'You will start a dogboy as I did. When you know what you're doing and why, you will be a dog man and call what you know skill. I think it will help getting you released.'

Returning him to Reverend Brown, I gave the high sign. He took Clee inside and came out with a notepad, taking down business address and phone number. He said he would arrange it with CYA for Clee to be sent weekdays with a bag lunch. I was to pay the van driver $5 in advance and Clee would be picked up noontime.

I returned to the patch. Not for Yukon I could have had fliers out and been doing business with locals, then with full occupancy increased the loan and brought in ten more hovels, taking in $90 a day seven days a week.

Making their snack at 9:45 I rolled the pony out the gate. Crying like never before, eeriness of a damp Sunday night frightened them even before I left.

.

Troubled back forth from Yukon to the dogs, feeling the full weight of neither made night go faster. Gone on first light I pulled uphill, counting them all. Cleaning the area, I fed walked brushed them. Noontime I called Jackson.

'Did he show?'

'Nah.'

I hurt for something to say.

'His head ain't in it,' said Jackson, 'he won't make it. They know first day if a rookie got a screw loose and waste no time on him. They call 'em *unaccountables*. Only thing they good for is gettin' people askin' *why?* What's the use you shellin' out? I don't feel right takin', surely you don't feel good payin'. What gets put in his hands he's gonna throw it to the ground. He's a boy-man; it's always what he gonna be and let what God gave him go.'

'Jackson, I have a dogboy coming to watch the patch. I'll bring Yukon to you to get going again.'

Tuesday Clee came with a bag lunch. Showing the van driver the business license I signed a statement of responsibility for which I paid $5. He said not to work him past noon and he would come for him before 1:30.

Dogs jumping about I took Clee to the workbench and had him open a can of Vets from both ends, push out meat roll, slice it in two and mix each half with a cup of dry meal. Opening four cans he fixed seven bowls, then opened a dented can of peas to mix into two bowls. They were to the hoarse white hound who coughed when he ate and the beagle, Blind Billy, who swallowed more than he chewed. Putting a bowl to each dog, his sullenness was not as repugnant to them as it was to humans.

After feedtime they were leashed in pairs for a walk. I thought he might warm to them by now. Bringing them one by one to the table I showed him how to use the brush. Not yet noon we could have sat for a little conversation but I determined to give him a lesson. Phillip left a portable slate at the side of the stoop from which he reminded himself. Ten active verbs I wrote having to do with animal care. I sensed they would enliven his muttering and we read them aloud.

I took him into the trailer to the pay phone.

'The door will be open when I'm not here. At a ring you are to answer, "I am Clee the dogboy. Daupin will soon be back. May I be of help?"'

I practiced him phone to his ear, his tone sullen but at least a caller would know somebody was around. The CYA van arrived, leaving hours on my hands before leaving the dogs to chance, then risk leaving them to Clee – that or give up on Yukon.

Heavy slumber weighing on, I put down on the flats, took the call at 3:30, slept an hour more before washing up. Gate rolling up I bumped down to daybreak and sped to the patch, jumping out to count the dogs. When Clee arrived I had done cleaning feeding walking. Taken to the stoop all he need do was sit there and answer the phone the way I taught him.

On to Yukon I pulled round the side of the old house to his hovel. Knocking, hearing nothing I turned the knob.

His head to the door did not go with leaving it open all night, the first thing a snooper would come upon. He would have slept past noon. Shaking sunlight he looked behind him and swung himself up.'

'Jackson told me you didn't show Saturday and Monday. The man was a professional football player and you don't show?'

'I lost the tokens.'

'You were without spare change to get on a bus? The tokens or nothing?'

He didn't answer.

'I'll come get you now. We won't let this fail.'

Buying another roll of tokens at the currency exchange I delivered him to Jackson. They got on the pads, went down the bank and knocked shoulders. Jackson told me to get five yards behind him and point the way.

Left right or straight on Yukon broke through or swung around, me dancing away not to be run down. Gathering himself Jackson had Yukon work on his stance. He talked to me not Yukon.

'I don't school him they'll think that Alaska Football he played was nuthin' but a gang rumble.'

Angling Yukon's stance from the squat he'd been getting into, he snapped him in and out.

I'd been been away over an hour and asked Jackson to make next time Friday. Three fifties I paid for the session and two wasted days, then gave Yukon a bus token to get home.

Clee was on the stoop eating from a bag lunch, gray morn turned sunny in every way.

'Anybody call?'

'Naw.'

Saying no more, I did not want him to get an idea how important it was to me that he watched the patch. The van come for him I took out my wallet and marked off 16th 17th 18th 19th 20th 21st 22nd. Taking out Cabe Nebo's number I phoned to a recorded message, trying again midnoon and eve. Half past nine I went out to give the dogs their snack, third to last night I would leave them. Saturday I had off, Sunday DiJi would return.

Hardening to risk I slept the night but hardly my blissful sleep there. Come back to the dogs, a sigh came out of me all its own. I could not have held it off for fifty dollars. I cleaned the ground and went into the trailer to call Cabe. Not yet seven I woke him.

'Mr. Nebo, Daupin here.'

'Who?'

'Daupin, we talked at the pool hall. I have Yukon training with Jackson Forte.'

'The wrestler?'

'Can you come see him?'

'Something don't smell right. Was he locked up? The way you describe him he sounds like an ex-convict to me.'

I could think of nothing I said to make him think Yukon did time.

'What I know is he worked in timber from 14 years old until he determined on wrestling.'

'I don't like a hunch I get here.'

'What good is a hunch if you can come look? You traveled the Midwest looking for a find. I have one right here at the park on 42nd. Jackson Forte works with him. I would think his opinion has value.'

'Call next week.'

The van brought Clee. We opened cans of Vets, mixing meat with dry meal. He remembered which dogs got corn in their bowls. He walked and brushed them. I brought over the slate. To his sour sniff I wrote out a rise-and-shine he could follow to be fresh to go each day.

They did not whine when I drove away that night, the chances of them being harmed now by a creeper down to two. I did the usual cleaning sweeping at the food bank, fixed a sandwich and slept. Showering after the call I got ready to go, my stomach tightening as the gate rolled up in new light.

Turning uphill I found them all out waiting. Gray dawn cleared to sunny morn the van brought Clee at 8:20. Cleaning feeding walking done, all he need do was to listen for the phone to ring and answer. Saying nothing he knew I was pulling a fast one.

Yukon's head to the door – why he didn't care to lock it I didn't ask – he snapped up. Watched over he toed the line. I drove him to Jackson sitting on his Seville. They worked for the second time on holding off a run block, with Yukon slamming his hands to Jackson's pads. Jammed by jolts that stopped him cold Jackson could not get to him. I paid for the session and handed Yukon a bus token saying I would come for him Monday.

Going to a seconds store I bought pillows sheets a blanket and bath mat. Back seat full I returned to the patch. Dogs all out and Clee on the stoop, I took the bedding inside and went out to level with him.

'Clee, I intend to bring in more dogs and give the place a name: Pooch Patch One. I mean to have many a Pooch Patch, numbering as I go. Since I can't be everywhere at once I want to count you in. You can become self-sufficient and have your own trailer and television. Does that give you hope?'

At a shift of his eyes I sat down beside him.

'I'll tell you something I've been saving. Do you remember, Clee, when you were a small boy and came across a field with your mama to a silver trailer and played with an older boy? It was *me*, Clee, I'm your cousin, *Daupin*.'

Raising his eyes to me he curled his lips in disgust.

The van come, the driver said he would bring him back Monday. Inside I rolled out the rug and made the bed with new sheets pillows blanket.

Daylong I cleaned in and out and worked on stains in the privy. To the dogs their snack, I coaxed them to stay calm one more night.

On to the food bank I could not rid myself of the notion of a poacher in the shadows when I'd closed the patch gate, too dull I'd been to get out and look around. Crossing off 23rd 24th I feared my luck running out and that very night bringing my comeuppance. All my will it took not to slip out and run back to the dogs on foot.

Showering after the call I looked through a *National Geographic*. The gate going up at six, the supervisor's nod sent me bumping down the ramp and wheeling the quarter mile like never before. Braking at the fence I swung back the gate and ran in counting all present. Hailing '*Halleluyagh!*' I turned east and spat three times like a poor Haitian does throwing off a curse.

The dogs were safe, Yukon back on track, DiJi due morrow plus I would sleep in the bed that night. I was seeing to them when a sportsman came for the hoarse white hound who was noisier than the others combined and best belonged on a farm. He owed for a day but I didn't bring it up so he might be inclined to return.

The sportsman of the Springer Spaniel showed, I feared he'd come to take him. Feeling around his flanks, surprised at how fit, he took a leather book from his pocket and wrote a check for July, $135, my first money there. Stroking sniffing this check for just one dog, I foresaw many more to come. Where but golden America, I asked myself, would someone pay $4.50 a day thirty in advance for the care of a dog?

Sunday afternoon DiJi arrived with Mammy and Theo, too excited to talk. Clearly told how to get to me – I pride in concise instruction – she phoned twice lost. Half a mile off they still couldn't figure the way. I drove to a Texaco off Adams Road, wheeling in with the top down. Mammy did not acknowledge my wave, bending an attendant's ear instead. DiJi waving from the camper I circled round pointing the way.

Leading them uphill I swung back the gate, inviting them in with a bow. Mammy and Theo smirked at what they had come to but DiJi ran up the stoop letting out a wild *whoop* at all the room for her things.

They were in the camper, foremost a table model television. I hardly would have thought a box made of wood and glass could be so ponderous. Hefting it between my chin and scrotum, its edges biting my hands and wrists like teeth, I climbed the stoop. Theo didn't budge. *'Move man!'* Clamping my teeth on a corner I backed around him through the door, skinning my knuckles before setting it down.

While DiJi and I brought in the rest he sat in the booth lapping cereal Mammy poured for him. As DiJi found a place for everything, the old hide griped about the pay phone, stage whispering DiJi was there to watch the dogs. DiJi phoned Mrs. Nelson and gave my directions there. We took time to walk down Adams Road talking about our start, a start spoiled by Mammy and Theo. After fixing the dogs their snack we kissed on the stoop to Mammy's smirk and I drove out the gate to my sanctuary. My sleep on cardboard flats made up for the past six, waking unknowning of who or where I was. I did not remember taking the call.

The dogs were not so happy to see me now that someone spent the night, not a one damp with dew. I shoveled up droppings, cleaned eyes ears, refilled water bowls and served breakfast.

Straddling them from behind I worked a rubber pick between teeth and gums. Creaks came from the trailer. DiJi in her robe stuck out her head. I went up the stoop to a whisper.

'Mammy wants to stay a week to see if I'm safe.'

I understood her concern. She was at the counter arranging goods from the camper. I sat with DiJi in the booth for coffee. Heaven it would have been were we alone.

Mrs. Nelson arrived. With a peck on my lips DiJi left for work. I sat with the dogs until the CYA van let Clee off.

'Clee, two visitors are here. You need not talk to them. If they get nosy say you must keep to your work.'

'You ain't supposed to leave.'

'Bear with me, Clee. You will be rewarded.'

I drove Yukon to the park. Jackson went at him only to be repelled by his long arms and red fists. He showed Yukon some hand jive, karate cuts to break off from a man close in, punches chops in combinations, telling him to take time to practice. Alongside like fellow defensive lineman they looped around one another.

Paying Jackson, I gave Yukon a bus token and drove to a pay phone. Eleven o'clock I didn't think I would catch him home.

'Mr. Nebo.'

'Who's this?'

'Daupin Capet. Jackson Forte and I have Yukon ready. We are at the park on 42nd at nine o'clock three days a week.'

'Not this week . . . make it Saturday . . . the 9th.

I counted June 27 to July 9. 'Is that early enough to arrange to get Yukon to a camp?'

'Let's bring you down to earth, pal. I've gone three years not recommending anyone. The league's gone superhuman. Physiques speed reflexes are more like that of an African herd beast than a man. Rookies come bred to the task, so the possibility of some raw hick imposing himself on the field is next to none.'

What he said did not discourage me. Returned to the patch I asked Clee if the white woman and her son in the trailer asked any questions. He said no and I went up the stoop and came in on Mammy poking holes in a slab of raw beef while Theo sat over a bowl of cereal watching the television I lugged in.

'Good morn, everything okay?'

'Well, where were you?'

'I have a project to look in on.'

'*Uhhum*, and you leave that boy to do your work.'

'He comes here to work for me.'

'*Massa, I'z comin' I'z comin* . . . ain't you the one?'

'Did the phone ring?'

'No.'

That's all I cared to know. I went out and pulled the slate to the workbench to give Clee another lesson in useful verbs until the van came for him. As he recited from the board, Mammy and Theo looked out with all the suspicion near illiterates have of forthright instruction.

211

DiJi come from work we sat down to eat. It was the slab of meat her mother had been torturing, boiled near leather, served with yams. My teeth cut on coarse food could not gnaw through. It let neither juice nor taste. Theo refused to eat it, having Mammy pour him a bowl of cereal.

DiJi said she was tired from the dogs barking all night and would not go for a walk. She got into her robe and slippers and we watched television with Mammy and Theo. Only one channel came in and the three of them sat enchanted by old drama shows, commenting on actors, especially those who'd been around. I sat with all the interest I would have in watching a spider climb a wall. Mammy went on about a neighbor's new television set until Theo could stand no more.

'She *got* no new color TV! She got that old black and white. She got a lot of junk, *that's* what she got! She sleeps on her couch in her coat!'

In the interest of equanimity I asked if he would come give the dogs a snack.

Yellow eyes flashed. '*I hate dirty filthy animals!*'

Halfway up my gall I went out to the workbench and sat a moment to calm myself. A biscuit and a massage across flanks and shoulders each of them got. DiJi appeared on the stoop, her arms around her.

'Daupin, tell me where you were today?' she whispered as I came up. 'Do you have a secret project going?'

Again I was not able to apprise her at a finer moment.

'DiJi, Jackson Forte, who Reverand Brown will affirm, is getting a wrestler named Yukon ready for a National Football League training camp. When he signs I'll take twenty percent. The minimum contract is $155,000, my cut thirty-one.'

'You'll get *thirty-one thousand?*'

'He signs a two-year contract it will be sixty-two.'

She pushed her glasses back.

'Why should you get all that money?'

'It was my idea. I put $200 a week into his training and board.'

'You pay *two hundred* a week?'

' DiJi, to make money you usually need to risk it.'

'Has he a chance?'

'He's a raw wonder, DiJi. Jackson says he's never seen anyone like Yukon. When a team sees him in action they'll sign him.'

She bit her lip.

'DiJi, I am thinking about keeping forty dogs and a brand new trailer in Florida with air-conditioning but I'll need your help. I'm impressed you bring in $200 a week for Reverend Brown. When Mammy and Theo leave we'll go further.'

Wednesday I got behind Jackson and motioned Yukon left right and straight on. He no longer hoped to block him, the best he could do, in his words, 'stick' him straight ahead or 'chip' him on the sides, jamming a shoulder into him to throw him off, but Yukon's charge did not break. He didn't bother now to drive Jackson back. Setting him on his heels he saw which shoulder was back and went through it like a turnstile. Jackson had a long weekend planned, which saved $50 I didn't need to spend. By the look of things Yukon was ready.

Friday I picked up 200 door hangers. On front I introduced myself as Daupin Capet doing business as Pooch Patch # 1, quality care, $4.50 a day, any dog any size any age welcome; on back: business license number and map bearing location on Adams Road.

I planned to hang them Saturday morn on Cermak Road before it opened for business, in that a merchant was more likely to board a dog than a workingman with a backyard and fence. DiJi whispered to take Theo and pay him a few dollars.

Taking from her voice how important it was to her I asked in front of Mammy if he would help. He turned from the television and followed me out. I watered and fed the dogs, driving out before seven, taking him to Dag's # 5. Instead of a sensible breakfast he wanted a burger fries malted shake. Indulging him for DiJi's sake I split the handbills, gave him half and pointed him west, ten blocks up one side then to return on the other, I to do the same east and then back to Dag's.

To brisk air I happily walked down Cermak hanging handbills. Crossing over with half left, I returned to Dag's emptyhanded only to find him at a table in back. A walk like I'd done would color anyone's cheeks. I saw no change in his.

'You hung the bills?'

'They gone. We gon' get more eats? I don't want what she cookin' back at the trailer.' He referred to Mammy only with dismissive pronouns.

I went to the cleanup boy.

'When did he come back in?'

'Hour ago, threw a bunch of hangers in the waste.'

I poked through plates and cups. Salvaging half the hangers I slapped them down in front of Theo.

'You said you hung these?'

'I hung some. What you gon' pay – $2, expect me to be walkin' up down the street?'

'Do you forget breakfast today and lunch spreads at Bob's Inn?'

'Oh, you gettin' DiJi and the red snapper but you countin' eats?'

I gave way to Gizmo, abandoning Good Daupin in mind and manner.

'You won't get more. No more here, no more at Bob's, no ride back neither.'

'You gon' give me a ride, awright, you took me here, you takin' me back.'

I thrust against the table. He gripped the sides wanting out. I turned out my jacket giving view of dybuk. All low class people fear being struck by their betters. Thinking I wouldn't dare he sank in the chair and kicked at my ankles. Two-handed overhead I slammed dybuk down. It would have split his skull.

'See what I got for you!'

Whistling through his nose he would get me, I smacked it down again, letting him know what he'd get if he tried. With the salvaged hangers I returned to DiJi still in robe and Mammy behind the counter.

'Where's Theo?'

'I left him.'

'*What!*'

'I left him. I gave him bills to hang and he threw them in the trash.'

'No *matter* what he did,' Mammy said, 'you just don't *leave.*'

'He won't get in my vehicle again, not anywhere.'

'*Where* is he?' she bawled. 'He don't do good left by hisself.'

'Dag's on 44 th.'

Like I'd left a child the old hide and DiJi ran to the camper and brought him back, not before calming him with a second burger fries malt. I could hear Mammy and him grousing in the trailer, trying to bring DiJi in on it. They were not going to leave without taking her out of there.

She came out to say she would be at her aunt's a few days. I did not ask why. It would only get worse there until Mammy and Theo were on their way home. Only through privacy and enterprise would we become one. Taking some things she got into the camper with them.

I sat on the stoop awaiting Cermak Road merchants to call. I'd hung a good hundred but the phone did not ring. Turning in early I stretched out on the sheets DiJi broke in and woke a new man with little more to do than bide time. Taking out my little calendar I saw now that in ambition there

215

is waiting beyond patience and in happenstance natural calm. All Sunday long the phone did not ring, not even a greeting from DiJi. Not as damp and eery as the past few Sunday eves, I fixed the dogs a snack and left for the food bank,

A black tramp awaited me, in a pick-up under a light pole. He had been there before timing my arrival, not the first big Negro to eye me, a lightskin scamp with tight curly hair – the law of the ghetto is that the big pray on the small in every way shape form. He made his move after the employees left, swinging a crowbar against the roll gate.

Bjang Bjang Bjang

Climbing up to a louvre I peered down at him in long coat, the pickup smoking behind him.

'What do you want!'

'Open up! Give a brother a break. Why you stand for the man?'

He looked drunk and could not follow my voice.

'I have a gun and a knife!'

'You ain' got shit, little ol' punk. I seen you ride up in yo' candy ass car. I want some what's mine.'

'Get in line like everybody else!'

Bjang Bjang Bjang

'Bitch, let me in . . . I get my hands on you . . .'

Climbing down I took the fire axe from the wall.

'Come through,' I called, 'I'll split your skull!'

He finally pulled away. I sat down to clear my head, looking over at my pony safe inside with me. Head on the table I slept until four, took the call, washed up and sat awhile longer. The gate rolled up, workers coming in with first light. Getting the nod I drove out.

Speeding to the patch I came upon a square-jawed mongrel tied to the gate. Friendly enough he was but looked like he'd been around. Untied he wouldn't go off so I fed him like the others, went in for a cup of tea and came back out to walk them. The van brought Clee and I drove to Yukon and

216

brought him to Jackson who didn't want to rush him until Cabe Nebo came Saturday. I would have gone along but Yukon showed color only when challenged and I aimed to keep it up.

Helmets and pads on they bumped shoulders and got to it. Five yards behind Jackson I beckoned Yukon around or straight on. Trying to dance him out Jackson was swiped away; setting himself he was run through. In twelve charges he could not hold him off once. He was too much for Jackson, too rangy in arms and legs, too stout in neck and chin. Usually Jackson had something to say, this time left still. I would have said something myself, but after what I saw I feared a hex.

On return I saw Cully stapling a poster to a telephone pole. Seeing another downroad I pulled to the curb to notice in orange and black of JULY 9th PRO WRESTLING AT THE ARMORY introducing WORLD TAG TEAM CHAMPS, SAMMO BROTHERS, along with Chicago All-Stars: *L'l All- America, Kilowatts, Jackanapes, Bullseye, Rick McDude, Hiram Schnapps, 8-Ball* . . . but no mention of Channel 4.

Returned to the patch with a notion Clee was hiding intelligence behind his scowl like he had in Miss Pierre's class I gave him a vocabulary quiz I tore out of a magazine. Sitting him at the workbench I went down a list of commonplace verbs, pronouncing each, offering three choices for a synonym, going down them all, giving every chance before concluding he lived in dark dismal thought I assumed was caused by glues sprays and other cheap intoxicants I read about in the newspaper. The van come for him I sat down to finances. I had a $135 check $285 in wallet $120 coming from the food bank Saturday. I would owe Jackson $100 for Wednesday Saturday and that would do it, leaving me $440 to get Pootch Patch # 1 to full occupancy. Everything had tidied out.

217

Come to the food bank I received notice my position would be eliminated July 8. I looked around at what had taken me from the cold, fed washed slept me like a mother a child. I consoled myself I could not succeed in canine board and care locked up there nights, sooner or later I had to go.

Back at daybreak I saw to the dogs and cooked a cup of tea. Clee arrived with no more to do than to leash and walk them. I did not leave the trailer open for him to answer the phone because of unfounded suspicion – shameful on my part for I pride in fairness – he would try on DiJi's heels and strut in the mirror.

I drove to the pool hall to find Cabe there. Told I missed him I searched *Yellowbook* for veterinary clinics, finding two in the area. Arriving I gave out handbills. Both with keep I asked I be called should they get more dogs than they could handle, getting only fishy looks in return.

Returned to the pool hall should Cabe stop back in, I sat awhile then returned to the patch, waiting for the van to come for Clee. I had no writing paper, but on a blank page at the end of the phonebook I drew up a contract:

I, Yukon Kid professional wrestler, will pay Daupin Louis Capet 20% of the considerations of my first contract as an NFL player or taxi-squadder in return for leading me to this endeavor and paying for my training.

Yukon Kid _____ date _____
Daupin Capet _____ date _____

Uneasy my night, on first light I sped from food bank to the patch, safer the dogs were with the square-jawed mongrel

218

there. I would have let him off the chain but he was a vagrant and would get over the fence and bring freeloaders. When the van didn't arrive by 8:30 I drove out to Yukon. This business of making Clee my kickalong was just about over anyway. I could not bring along a cousin who loathed me for no reason I could see.

Jackson faithful as always I thought better than to rush Yukon at this point but determined keeping his color up more important. Sore in the neck Jackson flinched straight on so I signaled Yukon round left right, his charge 45 degrees to the ground, fairly gliding, showing off it seemed were it possible of him.

I drove him to a notary. Blushing a potential NFL player was in his humble office, he looked over my writing, made changes, then had us sign date it. He suggested we might draw a more formal contract but I did not see how something as plain as our agreement would not hold up.

Taking him back to his hovel it occured to me he had little to do. I took $5 from my wallet.

'Don't stay in the room. Get an ice cream cone, walk around, buy a puzzle. Saturday the scout comes to see you. It will be over, you'll be on your way.'

'Hy Speed wants you Friday.'

'For what?'

'The run-through.'

'When did you see him?'

'Yesterday.'

'Did he say anything about Channel 4 coming back?'

'No.'

'I'll come for you.'

I took sudden hope Hy Speed signed a Channel 4 contract and Hugo insisted on me in part. DiJi would now send Mammy Theo home and we would be alone. We were a mismatch, sure, she a head taller – yet how many American dynamos pictured in financial magazines stood proudly with wives who towered over them yet said they felt fulfilled in every way?

Idle day ahead I got to thinking it was in TV, finally, my best prospects lay. Yukon signing with a team would leave me trusting – as Jackson suggested – on him going to the bank Mondays to cut out my pay. Far-fetched in cold light, but with signed agreement I felt I would get my share one way or another. Should he come to a second contract he would be acquainted and pointed away. I would be 'history' as they say in the pool hall. As a Pooch Patch operator I could easily manage a profitable patch on my own, oversee a second, possibly a third, but to go for broke I would have to depend on help as dutiful as I had been for Phillip, and I wasn't one who could count on others. A weekly wrestling gig would leave me to my own devises to come up with shenanigans to perform on TV Saturday nights and take home professional pay. Hugo said pay would be negotiable, the $289 day player contract Channel 4's ante to have a look at the cards. A regular show certain to pay more, I was sure Hugo wouldn't let me fall far behind the others. Five hundred dollars, even a thousand weekly hardly seemed out of line for a television show regular.

Fidgeting most of night I drove out to fine morn with thoughts of attaining such local notoriety for Gizmo I could take him to the New York show. Set there I might approach TV big-wigs for advice in changing course for I did not want to be a wrestling show buffoon past age 35. If television news was not realistic for my limited background perhaps I could see a way into a co-ordinator position like Hugo's. Eve I'd had my fill and drove to the food bank. Morrow I would know if my start in television arrived.

Taking the call I lay still awhile, then showered and wiped windshield and side glass. The gate rolled up I made for the patch, finding the dogs slept better than me. Seeing to them, I sat until the van brought Clee.

Driving out to Yukon I pulled onto the gravel aside his hovel, when his landlord ran outside in his shabby robe, leaving his wife atop the fire stairs.

'Mister Gizmo, *please!*'

I feared something had happened.

'Last night – middle of night – the tenant you brought us let out a scream not of this world. Our blood turned cold. We lay in bed shaking.'

'You sure it was him?'

'Below it came.'

'People scream asleep.'

'This was not a scream from a normal person, a scream a crazy man's. We thought he would come kill us.'

'Why would he kill you?'

'A crazy man needs a reason? My wife did not hear a scream like this in Buchenwald. I am a man, too – I could stand in his way? A giant! He could kill us like two chickens. Mr. Gizmo, we are scared!'

'You have no good reason.'

I tried to turn away.

'Mr. Gizmo, please, something else. There is a private toilet.' He pointed under the stairs. 'It is his. We do not go in. We look Sunday, a *shtick* in the water would not go down. My wife asked if this came from a human being. I took gloves – with my hands I took it behind the bushes.'

'July 15 or so he's out.'

I nudged the door open on beer cans at my feet.

'What's this?'

He looked over his shoulder. 'I drank a few, I couldn't stop.'

I counted. 'So you drank twelve? You're a big galoot, you want a beer, *okay*: one, two. After that it's pisswater. This is what I gave you $5 for? You knew I was coming you didn't care if I saw this. There's only so much I can do. Afterwhile it's at your own discretion.'

221

He sat up.

'The landlord stopped me. A scream last night turned his blood cold. Are you getting nightmares, cold sweats?'

'Nah.'

'You remember letting out a scream?'

'I slept.'

I drove with the top down to wake him. Red hair blowing it looked he rode in a rich schoolboy's toy. A dozen vehicles awaited us at the armory. Getting out I was berated by a loudmouth behind the wire fence.

'Gizmo! Punk ass Gizmo!'

I ignored him, fearing for my roadster, a small natural target like me. The retired slouch sitting by the door would not so much as shift his haunch to protect someone's property.

Marquees were in the rear with take-out, each in his glory but today deferring to a new one, Sonny Sammo, a Pacific Islander pushing five hundred pounds from his chest. He stalled and Romeo, his tag team partner and so-called *brudda*, 'spotted him' in marquee lingo. A cast over left arm and shoulder Romeo hooked a finger under the bar, coaxing it up. Replacing the weight Sonny Sammo let out a howl that would have put a passerby in the corridor in fear of a madman. We were accosted by Up'n'Up Barry.

'Hy brought in the Sammos to jump up the show! You're the match. He's got it going now: Pizza Italiano signed up, *Wrestling Bible* is coming for a pictorial. He's on the phone with *Rasslin' Flash* for highlights.'

'What about Channel 4?'

Before he could answer we were called in to Hy who handed Cully the phone.

'I did a work-up for *Wrestling Bible*. Gizmo, you were in Alaska in a Piper Cub with a bush pilot. What you were doing there, God knows? The plane goes down, pilot's smoked, you're pinned down in the snow with white wolves all around ready to tear your ass to pieces. Suddenly the place is on the skids: wolves flying in the air, running for their lives. You look up thinking a bear's come to finish you off and see a red giant lifting a wing off you. He carries you to his hut and you see he has the mind of a child. He plays with gold nuggets like marbles. So how do you repay him? You steal his gold, teach him pidgin English and take him to a crooked lawyer to sign a personal services contract where you control everything he has, says and does. Got it?'

'I don't need much to go on. Any news on Channel 4?'

'What news are you expecting?'

I feared to answer.

'They're history.'

He put out two waivers.

'Sign and date. You go against the Sammos.'

Following him out to the marquees around the weight bench, Yukon was put to Sonny Sammo with bushy brow and Java Man jaw.

'This some ridge runner, lumberjack dude?'

Hy Speed answered, 'Alaska wildman. Gizmo here found him shitting in the woods like a bear and programmed him. Gizmo controls his every move. He doesn't know right from wrong.'

Sonny sized him up. 'One big brute . . . but are you bad?' He stood up no taller than five-eight.

'O.K., it's gonna be brief but brutal.'

Yukon took off his shirt. Sonny looked over his shoulder 'distracted.'

'I'm turned at my no-good brudda cruisin' seats for fine young ladies. Come up on my back, run me.'

Yukon took his blocky hand.

'Stomp! Stomp!' called Sonny.

Stomping a foot Yukon veered Sonny around.

'Lay your shucks.'

Yukon brought a forearm down on his back, a knee up against his hip.

'Hoo Choo! Hoo Choo! Five six times.'

Yukon alternated forearm knee.

'Post to post.'

Yukon trotted him in a square, 'whipping him into corners'. Once it got going it looked like a large lunatic in an asylum abusing a smaller one. He brought him back to start.

'Five six jams to the buckle,' Sonny ordered up.

Yukon took him by the back of the neck. Sonny shrunk in his hand.

'My *head* not my neck. Every wrestler got damage in the neck. First thing you learn, brudda.'

Gripping his head Yukon threw it to a 'turnbuckle'.

Sonny's hair snapped forward. Yukon threw his head again and again to Sonny's rage. Then his head would not budge. Shoulders square, nostrils afire he'd had enough.

'My eyes go big I go off on you, brudda, I get notorious with you.'

Turning on Yukon he whipped a chunky hand across his throat.

'Sell it!'

Yukon doubled over. Sonny caught his arm, spat in his palm and slammed it into the hollow of Yukon's neck and shoulder. It popped like a beef joint over flame.

'Now I lay shucks, brudda. Pop! Pop! Pop! Ten fifteen in a row, brudda, peckerheads picking up the count. Hoo Choo! Hoo Choo! You tall, brudda, I chop you short. I shake your hand, brudda, but I stretch you out. I paid mine, that's for real. I know every martial arts there is and can jump nine feet in air like Charles Manson.'

Romeo gave a war whoop and Sonny's eyes fell on me.

'What tomfoolery you bringin' to bear, brudda?'

I pulled out dybuk. 'It's going bad for Yukon I can come out with this.'

'What in all hell is that?'

'A bull deek.'

224

'A bull dick for real?'

'I can hustle it an inch from a man's nose.'

'You hustlin' nuttin' at my nose, brudda.' He turned to Hy. 'You keep chicken blood or strangle powder?'

'I got powder and pump.'

'So I'm layin' shucks in the corner and pimp boy here climbs up and blasts my eyes. Now big boy brings it, hands on my traps, thumbs in my throat.'

Yukon gripped the humps of Sonny's shoulders.

Sonny waved to one and all. 'Blind in one eye, chokin', head rollin', only thing left, brudda, only thing I ever trusted and believed in – my Islander strength.'

Throwing a shout he wrung himself out of Yukon's grip and swung around behind him hooking an arm across his throat. Tilting him back in a strangle he sapped Yukon's hip and stomped his heels.

'Dance! Shake a leg, bitch!'

Yukon flopped his legs. Loaming from the mouth he slapped Sonny's arm to let go. I ran over and grabbed on.

'He's choking!'

Yukon being wheeled on his heels I was swung into a whack on the forehead from Romeo's cast, falling to my knees with just enough light in my eyes to see Yukon's eyes rolling back in his head. Air ripping through his crotch he shat and wet his jeans and dropped on all fours.

'He pissed his pants, popped his shit,' I heard all around me.

'Breathe in, breathe out.' called Hy speed slapping his back, waving me over.

'Clean him up at the custodial sinks. Go!'

Taking his shirt I helped Yukon up just as Cully came out of the office.

'Rasslin Flash's comin'!'

Escaping hoots and yells I led Yukon down the corridor to custodial where a row of wash basins ended at a shower stall.

'Get your boots off, go in with your pants.'

Boots and socks discarded he braced against a rush of water.

'Take 'em down.'

Pulling out of the dungarees he held them up to water pounding the crotch. I unscrewed the handle of a pushbroom and stuck it out.

'Let's have 'em.'

He hung on the jeans and I swung around.

'Stay here till I get back.'

'Where'm I gonna go?'

Going to my pony I laid them on the rack over the trunk, winding the legs through the bars. A knot on my forehead the size of a walnut I steered around behind a coin laundry downroad and hoisted the trousers. A Viet Cong-looking guy saw me coming.

'Di ra bhor day! Cut di! Di ra bhor day! Cut di!'

I went by him through the door and dropped the pants into a machine. While he yapped in my ear I found the dollar changer and soap. Joining him his wife pointed to the water I tracked in. I turned away from their snapping teeth but it was no use. Pulling out dybuk I cracked him one. He staggered to the front holding his head, his wife screaming after him. The only other patron took flight out the door.

Standing guard at washer dryer, I folded the jeans and returned to the armory, coming in on Yukon on a stool with tarpaulin across his back.

'He put me in a choke, I couldn't get out.'

'Houdini couldn't have got out. It says something you didn't black out.'

Handing him the jeans I sat down.

'Why'd he do that to me?'

'Who do you think you're dealing with? Gym bums, con men, you heard their talk . . . how they hung around gyms selling muscle jive to idiots who wanted to look just like them? Times got tough and Jackanapes went on a construction job and with all those muscles quit after two hours saying he'd go to jail first, jail before honest labor. I see you trying to get acquainted but they ignore you. They don't want to teach you their dirty little tricks yet. You have a chance to go to an NFL camp, do battle, make thousands of dollars —'

'Gizmo, you wanna hang on me?'

'*Hang* on you?' Hard of breath the answer came on its own. 'I'm five foot two with a bent leg. My mother wasn't born whole. I led her around when I was four. My Granme boiled long boxes of Blue Cross Spaghetti with shank bones to feed us. Twelve years old I ran suits downtown to bring home a few dollars. I looked around with big eyes at all the stores wondering how anybody ever got the money to open one . . . then day by day block after block it came to me – you don't need a store and line of goods to do business. You can do business seeing something in somebody nobody else can – working it, shaping it, bringing it to bear on the public – and if you can do that you stand fast with any man-jack who owns twelve department stores . . . you make your own way, you hang on no one.'

I drove him back.

'*Morrow* nine o'clock at the park. Look here!'

His head turned.

'Cabe Nebo will be there. You can leave all this behind and be on your way. It rides on you. I can be of no more help. I'll come at eight. Be outside. Don't have me come get you.'

Mammy's camper was back. Clee sat in shade cracking nuts in his teeth. He watched you with one eye (contempt) or both (suspicion). I pulled up, he turned half away. Giving the dogs a look, I went up the stoop.

DiJi was in her bathrobe, her glasses slipped on her nose. She had not gone to work with Mrs. Nelson. Mammy was at the counter tormenting another slab of meat.

'Look who's here, Massa Gizmo.'

'When are you leaving?'

'Next week, okay by *you?*'

I meant Theo behind her. 'He's going to sit there all day watching television and lapping cereal?'

'Do I recall you passing your plate after Sunday blessings? "Oh, looks good! More chicken please, don't forget the cornbread!"'

'What's wrong, DiJi?'

'She's disturbed, that's what's wrong. She says you spend all your money on a white boy.'

'My wrestler Yukon, no two men can hold him. He trains for football. Morrow comes a scout. He will be on his way to fame and fortune.

'What if he can't make it?'

'No can'ts! He's a raw wonder. Six-six and a half, eighty-eight inches arms wide, the *look* of him alone. *Can't* you see what I've got going here? I have room for twenty dogs. In time I will set up in Florida and range out. No decent man will leave his dog in a cage.'

'And who's gonna do the work while you gallivantin' in that little red car – DiJi and the boy out there? You're not even payin' him.'

'I pay the state $5 a day. They're glad to bring him.'

'And he don't get a penny, do he? Slavery's over, mister. Mr. Lincoln freed the slaves.' She went to the door and called Clee.

'Don't be scared, Mammy's here!'

Clee stuck in his head.

'What are you paid for working here?'

'Food and water.'

Reaching over I shut the door in his face.

'DiJi says you call him dogboy.'

'Before you become a dog man you start a dogboy. That's how I started. I took time to give him a vocabulary test. He scored a 2. The lump behind you would score higher. Still I don't hold by that. I take the slate and give instruction, and I'll teach DiJi how to run the patch, receive animals and take payments. I promise to make her a business woman —'

'*All* these promises. Dub Fuller asks about DiJi whenever he sees me. He said if DiJi came back he wouldn't care what his family said or church people thought. Some other young white men wanted her and wouldn't give a good doggone what nobody said.'

'*Wanted* her? They want to get all up in her, that's what they want – make her a farm wife. Farmers work their women hard – *many* a way. They are out all day watching what sheep and bulls do then come home with the same look in their eyes. *That's* what you want for DiJi? Don't you see a future in all the things I have going? One day I'll have Pooch Patches by the number. I'll market Gizmo dog food. I'll build a headquarters.'

'You have a job in mind for Theo?'

'Sorry, I can't use him.'

'He only screwed you up once.'

'I *can't* use him! He's a flake! You want me to spell it out? I felt sorry for him. I bought him a burger fries malt and he reamed me.'

'You won't never do nuthin' for Theo?'

Lapping from the bowl he looked over.

'Let's see: 26 years old living with his mother, never had a girlfriend, don't seem to want to . . . smacks odd, don't it? Could be innocent in its own right . . . but a full grown man eating his mother's food, don't have a job, don't want a job, not even thinking about one? You could just say this individual is lazier than steaming hot shit coming out a field hand's ass on a frosty morn.'

229

He grabbed the meat fork from Mammy and came at me, all eyes and buttocks.

'He's not worth it. He ain't worth it.'

I ran out the door, jumped the stoop and cut across the patch with him after me. In a swoop I unhitched the white mongrel and charged him by the collar. Turning tail the red pig ran back up the stoop with Mammy and DiJi whipping the door shut behind him.

Dog in one hand, dybuk in the other, I called him out.

'Come at me with a meat fork in my own house and home? I'll have your rind!' I cracked the air. 'Come out, I will fight you!'

Not moving a muscle Clee stayed right where he was. The CYA van came and I drove to the pool hall should Cabe Nebo drop in. He sang himself a high one for having to do no more than take a twenty-minute ride for a look at Yukon. Beholding him morrow morn would change his tune.

Waiting out light rain I feared heavier fall to follow and Cabe Nebo not showing up. Driving to the food bank I found rest on the flats, sleeping through, going down the ramp daybreak under pale sky.

Seeing to the dogs I kept one eye on camper and trailer lest the red pig run out with a weapon. On to the pool hall I sat over coffee. Cabe need only show up and Yukon would set him straight. I was almost afraid to get it over with.

He was at the curb, a good sign until I saw he was unshaved unslept. I did not ask why. It did not matter now.

'Can we stop to eat?' Beer was on his breath.

We got to the park under sky so low I smelled rain. They were on the grass, an odd pair for having played the same position in the National Football League, round chunky Cabe and Jackson long of neck and arm with a heavy trunk.

'Cabe Nebo,' I told Yukon. 'Steelers and Eagles guard in the Fifties and Sixties. He likes what he sees you'll go to an NFL camp.'

Out of the pony Yukon filled Cabe's eyes.

'Yukon Kid,' I announced.

Cabe tried getting a smile out of him.

'You've been knocking heads with Jackson?'

Jackson had to answer for him.

'A rumble every day, he come like a freight.'

Cabe's second look at Yukon told me he thought this all a joke. He glanced up at the sky.

'Let's see.'

Unzipping his bag Jackson harnessed Yukon. I tugged the blue jersey over his pads and handed him the Oiler helmet. Jackson snapped on his Pro Bowl helmet. Putting a newspaper under him Cabe sat down on the bank while I felt around at wet grass. Bicycle boys stopping on the walk above, Cully pulled up to the curb in his meter hack and stuck out his head. Yukon and Jackson squared off. It had come.

Getting five yards behind Jackson I beckoned Yukon straight on. He lunged into Jackson, knocking him back before slipping to his knees. Next I waved him right and he swung out but couldn't get around. Jackson danced him away. I motioned him left, what Jackson expected. Letting him get a leg around he 'split him out.'

It looked he was getting no traction. It had rained enough to slick the grass but the cake underneath did not give. His worn out work boots took no grip.

Waved straight on he slipped again and stood up looking lost. Cabe laughed to himself. Only a white man does it just right, a twinkle in the eye with it. At the curb Cully grinned out the window. Slipping was not his fault but being unslept unwilling was. Remembering his coarse gray socks when he sat on the mattress on the bus, I called over 'Take off your boots, this is going nowhere!'

Getting that blank look of his I had half a mind to walk away.

'Take off your boots.'

Hands on hips he went aside and took them off. Pulling up those same socks, he faced back with Jackson. I signaled to come straight again, not really expecting much better. He shot out nearly rolling Jackson over. Scampering back on his heels like a barefoot boy Jackson chased me out of the way. I signaled Yukon to his strong foot, which Jackson expected, Trying to dance him out he was turned upside down. Up on his knees he tapped his head to see if it was still there.

Jackknifed, rolled, flung aside, run through, run over, spun, swung like a sack, slammed on his back, stood still and left behind Jackson could barely lift a hand in defense. Yukon's legs scissored with such strength as to break a man's arm caught between them. Two Jacksons could not have held him off. Three would have had a time. Cabe took back the grin. Cully pulled away. Evil omen gone, sunlight broke through.

'The bull rush again,' called Cabe. 'Jaw to jaw.'

Jackson bulled his neck and Yukon dug in on all fours. I crouched to my knees.

'*Get set, go!*'

Helmets clapped together like a .22 going off in a tin shooting gallery. Jackson's cleats raked rearward, upending sediment until he took flight, bouncing on his back to me with Yukon leaping clear. Backpeddaling I held my hands out to stop him.

'Take off the helmet, put on your boots and walk around.'

Lucky his neck wasn't cracked Jackson went up on the bank and sank down on the grass.

'You givin' ground?' Cabe asked.

'I wouldn't give my brother ground. He gets ahold of you he takes you out like a forklift.'

'You've been out ten years.'

'Straight on I take the same lick I ever could. I never went against anybody this strong. He's bigger than they were too.'

'How big is he?'

'Six-six and a half, two sixty-six,' I put in.

'All bone,' said Jackson. 'Feels sharp, hurts your hands. He put on forty pounds he'd be so strong it'd be against the law. How you can be that big and turn on a dime I don't know.'

'He started in timber camps when he was fourteen,' I said, 'climbing trees, rolling logs.'

'How old does he say he is?'

'Twenty six.'

'He's thirty, I'll let it go. He's got no college?'

'He played with the pipeline gangs in Alaska and got paid.'

'Some sell,' hummed Cabe. 'My day they'd dress a goon. Even five years ago a strapper could still hang on a year or two on how he filled out a uniform. That's closed up.'

Jackson helped out. 'Cabe, we both know if a man can get to a quarterback, a whole lotta shit falls wayside. You tellin' me a DL guy sees what you saw his eyes won't —'

'Tell me what's missing. I'm not getting the whole picture.'

Jackson formed some thought. 'Sumthin' ain't right in his head. All the work we done it's like he sees me first time. His eyes don't acknowledge you. I played with hardcases, killers even; sooner or later they come out a little. I was raised to be friendly, I'm a team guy, I usually get to an individual.'

'He's been on his own since twelve,' I said. 'Nobody wanted him. He was too big. He told me he used to cover himself with leaves and sleep off road.'

Jackson tapped Cabe's knee. 'You asked if I was holding back, I think he was going easy on me.'

233

Cabe stood up at some rain, holding the paper overhead. 'Call me next week.'

I held him up, 'A team wants to see him, how's it done?'

He gave a dubious look after what he just saw. I didn't like him.

'They send an airline voucher and camp pass.'

'What do you think?' I asked Jackson as Cabe hustled off.

'He'll know what to say.'

Jackson said he would be taking medical tests that week and could work with Yukon only Tuesday and that would probably do it before he went to camp. I paid him, helped Yukon off with the jersey and pads and took him up to the curb.

'It won't be long. Camps start in eight days or so. Why take a chance with Sonny Sammo tonight?'

'What if I don't make it? Wrestling's all I got.'

'Nobody there will hold you off. Maybe older guys can take you on but you'll manhandle new guys. *Why* can't you see that like I do? When the coaches get a look they'll waste no time signing you. What's the use in showing up to face Sonny Sammo for $50? He's cruel and knows how to hurt someone.'

'I don't depend on nuthin' but what's up front, I never had luck with me.'

I pulled into the patch and called to DiJi in the trailer. Come to the porthole she saw two gift certificates held up in my hand.

'It's done, DiJi! Time to celebrate. We're going to the matches, then to Shrimp Grill for supper and cocktails.'

She turned away a moment. 'Mammy and Theo want to come.'

'They can stay with the dogs.'

'They want to see wrestling?'

'They won't ruin our night!'

'They're not going, I'm not.'

'DiJi, Yukon is going to a training camp. We need to be alone. I feel this is our last chance.'

Theo took her place. 'You ain't no man. You didn't come from woman. A tramp shit you out in an alley.'

I swung out dybuk. 'Want some, fat butt?'

'Bitch, ol' lame bitch!'

'DiJi, don't do this! Tonight's our night!'

She returned with Mammy's words in her mouth.

'All of us or none!'

I saw to the dogs, stopped for a red hot, then drove to the armory. Yukon came over beside me, knowing now I was all he had there.

Hy Speed grabbed my arm.

'Let's go.'

I followed him to the prop cage in the utility room where he retrieved an old shoot-from-the-hip fumigater painted with skull and crossbones. Pumping out talcum clouds I was told to go put it under the stoop.

I got Yukon out in the corridor before the Sammos came.

'He choked you once he'll try it again. He does the reverse, get your fist up under your chin. Let him try choking you like that. You're stronger than he is, go the routine, no more. His so-called brother jumps in I'll be there this time.'

Turning out my jacket I showed him dybuk. 'No one-arm man takes Gizmo when he has his sap. I'll do a job on his skull. It's our last go here, we have to come out okay.'

Almost a full house to see the Sammos, Red Canyon jested with one and all Up'n'Up Barry, then Kilowatts came up into the ring, Barry showing clean moves before Kilowatts turned him upside down and piledrove him with such thumps Barry's scrotum popped out of his trunks. To howls of laughter he waved his arms he'd had enough and was dropped on his head. Coming back up the ramp he barely acknowledged me.

Next two matches went as usual, a feisty jobber slapped around and stretched out. Up next Yukon and I went into the ring. To a trumpet's charge Hy Speed ran interference for Sonny Sammo with his championship belt slung over his shoulder, followed by Romeo waving his balsa war club. Rabble going wild Hy spread the ropes and Sonny danced in to 'Jimmy Crack Corn.' It dimmed and Terry Donley made the call.

'In blue corner from the wilds of the North Country, managed by his Svengali, Gizmo, a svelte 266 pounds – Yukon Kid.'

Rabble howling to the rafters, Terry Donley swung acround.

'Opposing in red corner, one half of World Tag Team Champion Maui Ridgerunners, at a slippery 250 pounds, give a Chicagoland welcome to the great Sonny Sammo – accompanied by championship partner and brother, Romeo.'

Holding Sonny's belt overhead Hy took his leave. The bell didn't send Sonny into action, distracted he was by Romeo cavorting with two floozies. Yukon drove him headfirst into a post, letting him have it forearm and knee, a stomp and *'Haw!'* with each blow. Me waving him on he ran Sonny corner to corner, slamming his head. Hair flying, Sonny called to Romeo who was 'unaware' of the beating his brother was taking. A look come into Sonny's eyes, rabble jumping up and down for him to come around. Yukon gripped his head like a grapefruit, this time it did not budge. Sonny's rage had built to insanity. I yelled for Yukon to finish him but Sonny turned in his face, chopped his hands across his neck and swung him around into the stoop post.

Taking backhand after backhand Yukon sagged on the ropes above me. It was time. Getting under the apron I brought out the blaster. Rabble shouting *Watch out!* I came up

236

the stoop, peeked around Yukon's back into Sonny's crazed eyes and pumped twice in his face. *Graagh!* Dusted white he choked and spat, gripping his throat. Yukon got him around the neck lifting him straight up. Jaws clenched, face afire, Sonny pried Yukon's fingers apart and fell loose. Yukon tried to grab ahold again but Sonny swung around behind him hooking an arm around his throat. Rabble jumped for joy at the *Maui Sleeper*, no man could break it. Ducking around the stoop to see if Yukon did what I told him to, I tasted something hard and bitter on my teeth.

Down on my knees my sore eyes flickered up at Romeo and the balsa club I bit into. Overhead Sonny had Yukon bent back over his heels, hissing to him to pull his fist out from under his chin but he wouldn't go along and was dropped to the mat. Pinching a split lip I sneezed blood from my nose and climbed through the ropes, helping Yukon to his feet.

Leading him up the ramp we were hit by hard candy and balled paper cups with pennies. In the utility room I ran water over my mouth and packed tissue under my bottom lip. Come a little higher Romeo would have cost me two three teeth.

'It's behind us now,' I said.

Taking our pay I drove him to his hovel, then pulled up in front of Emil's to turn in. NFL camps opening in a week or so, it was only to hear from Cabe now.

A week I thought to catch my breath went bad for me. A sportsman encountering Clee took his two dogs, then called two other sportsmen to tell them about the low-class caretaker left in charge. Midnoon they came, Diji Mammy and the red pig looking on as I stood there with a split lip refunding $45.

That left three, one of them the square-jawed mongrel. Mammy and Theo were still there for the sole purpose of taking DiJi home to marry one of those farmer bachelors Mammy bragged about who would mount her each night like a bull a cow. When Clee arrived in the CYA van next morn he saw his time there almost run out.

237

Tuesday I brought Yukon to Jackson who had him snapping in out of three-point stance. Using me as decoy he showed him to watch for a blindside should he find himself in the open, I myself knowing a thing or two about that. He turned his palms up, training Yukon done.

I took out a fifty but Jackson said that one was on the house. I drove Yukon back to 74th.

'We'll get news any day. Get all else out of your head, Hy Speed, Sonny Sammo, the cot here. Look forward now. When you make a team you can buy a good car, find a girl and give her a house and home. You won't be alone again.'

'I can't make a family. My testicles were crushed when I was eight.'

'How do you mean crushed?'

'Crushed! They don't work.'

'You've been to a doctor?'

'I know myself. I can't do with a woman. I can't have kids.'

I felt my head wobble. What was in all striving did it not lead to hearth and home?

'Don't stay inside,' I mouthed. 'Walk around, think of what's ahead for you.'

Barely away I pulled over. I'd pushed him into something he didn't want, unbeknown to me he was crippled too. It meant more now that he should go on and make a team than getting my twenty percent. I had taken him too far.

When I got to the patch Mammy's camper was not there.

'DiJi!'

'They gone,' called Clee from the workbench.

I looked around inside. All her things taken including the television, I could not imagine how they got it out. Finding no note I went out on the stoop, noticing the slate turned backward. Turned around, upon it was chalked:

238

Gizmo a Punk
Gizmo a big Punk
Gizmo all de Punk deh is

Thinking Theo did this I just as quickly doubted he would make the effort. Waving Clee over I took ahold of his arm.

'Who wrote this?'

'*Unhand me, man!*'

Seeing what I tapped against my leg he changed his tune. Letting loose of him I went to the hovels and stuck a finger in the bowls.

'You like drinking warm water, Clee?'

'Naw.'

'They don't either. They like the same water you do, cool and clean.'

Blind Billy came out of his hovel but the mongrel was gone.

'Where's the white one?'

'He climbed over and ran off.'

I'd seen a pack roving around a shuttered K-mart down Independence Road. Wheeling down a long hill I trolled a grown over lot, scaring half-wild dogs out of the weeds. On to the pool hall I sat an hour for Cabe to come by. When I returned to the patch Clee was gone.

The CYA van didn't come Wednesday. Calling why, I was told Clee Doss said he was threatened with a weapon. Asked if I had something for the record before a report was sent to the police station, I said no thanks.

Determined to see Yukon off, if it took every minute of the day, I called the numbers of the two dogs left and asked that they be picked up as soon as possible with refunds. The owner of the Springer Spaniel came. Apologizing for short notice I refunded $65 for care not tendered, saying I would open again, if he cared to bring him back.

'Hardly,' he sniffed.

Only the blind beagle left I waited for the owner all day. Calling Cabe next morn to no answer I drove to the pool hall finding him with his DP pals. He took me aside.

'They'll look at him.

'Who?'

'Not so fast, *who!* I want a thousand.'

'For what?'

'I'm sending him on my word. He flakes out who'll trust me again? Who knows his background; if he's even intelligent enough to understand a defensive scheme?'

'He's a natural, he'll make it.'

'Hey, pal, every coach ever has had a *natural* who drove him nuts – a goon who won't let himself go – a stiff. They're off the map, *extinct!'*

'Cabe, I'll pay down the line.'

'Up front! People say, "Cabe, you were with the Eagles, you were with the Steelers. You don't have a care in the world." I got cares and bills both. I go at risk here. This guy don't look right in the head like Jackson said. A camp pass comes Special Delivery. You don't ante up I'll cancel it.'

I drove to 41st and Ashland finding Jackson in an apron sweeping out the tavern. If he'd watched his money he'd own the place; he didn't so he swept it out.

'What're you doin' here, little brother?'

'Cabe wants a thousand to get Yukon to camp.'

He did not look surprised.

'Can you contact your old teams?'

'After my disability claims they cut off from me. They used to send jackets, promotional gear.'

'Is anyone you played with coaching now?'

'A few got positions – Grambling, Black schools . . . Hold on! I ran into Roye Matzak at Spring Fest.'

'Roye Matzak! He's a Chicago guy?'

'He's sculpting at the university. He gave me his number.'

He went behind the bar, dumping business cards from a bowl.

'I been meanin' to call.'

Trying a number to no answer he told me to call him later.

I returned to the patch thinking if I only knew the training camp I would put Yukon in my pony and take him myself, but Cabe knew he was dealing with a go-getter. I called the owner of the blind beagle again. His wife said he would come by. I expected him to be angry but he calmly stepped out of his vehicle and did not reject my apology. Free of responsibility I called Jackson.

'He wants you to come see him.'

'When?'

'Tonight.'

'With Yukon?'

'Just you.'

'Why not Yukon?'

'He said you for now. He's by Chicago Circle, go about seven.'

I took down the address. It wasn't easy dealing with sports people, everything done in parts. You couldn't just lay it all on the table like an honest man does. To me it was no way to do business.

Thinking how to represent Yukon to a former defensive charger and Super Bowl player, I drove out, stopping short of downtown and turning into the University area, much of the surroundings leveled for urban renewal. Finding my way to a refurbished building I faced a glass door and pushed *R. Matzak 211.*

'Who goes?'

'Gizmo, Jackson Forte's friend!'

Getting a buzz I went to the second floor, down to the last door hearing scuffing sounds inside. It opened on a man six foot eight with high frizzy hair, beside whom Yukon would look like a younger brother. He held close to a sharp white dog clawing floorboard. Recognizing the breed I was pointed down narrow aisle to kitchen.

'Go!'

He followed closing a gate behind him. I meant to shake hands but he took me around the shoulder.

'I need you to sit down. I'm taking a Bordeaux cooking class; I'm gonna try pork chops on you.'

I felt my face glow at his hospitality. Putting on an apron he uncovered two raw chops.

'You eat pork, don't you? You're not Muslim?'

'Oh, no!'

'My last year in football Muslim teammates asked me to join in prayer. I was even considering committing to Islam but you can't very well be a Muslim if you like pork chops, can you?'

'Hardly.'

He filled a wine glass, a Super Bowl knucklebuster on his hand.

'Caby I picked up at Trader Jim's, savvy not rude.'

'Must be a foreigner.'

He put the glass to me.

'Mmm!'

The dog wanted in. 'Schutzhund, isn't he? I'm a dog man myself. I'm in the business.'

He marveled, 'You must be to know that. I got him across the line from Germans in Wisconsin. Five apartments took in dogs. Two tenants were raped on the ground floor – one a man.'

'A man?'

'Intruders got through the window and tied a couple down on the bed. The guy thought that's as far as it goes with him. Before he knows it his pants are pulled, his buttocks spread and the fires of Vesuvius were in his eyes.'

'*Sick! Sick!* I hope they were caught and imprisoned.'

'Two little dudes.'

'They should have come through your window. It would have been a bad day at Black Rock for them.'

He cocked an eye. 'Two hellbent scamps determined to get their way will turn a big man inside out, I'll tell, ya.'

I did not know how to respond.

'Jackson Forte calls he has a guy Yukon or Alaska, a wrestler who wants to play ball, then tells me about a commercial little guy, Gizmo, who has a hundred things going. I say let wrestler guy wait. I want to meet the little dynamo. He sounds phenomenal.'

'Thank you.'

'Little men are so resourceful. I say that and I'm as big as they come. On the road my roommates were placekickers, my favorite Ebi Aziz, educated in Lebanon, trained in Libya to fight Russians in Afghanistan. All in one little dude. He came up a bathhouse boy in Turkey and when it comes to service there – excuse me not – no holds barred. Massage is capped off leaving not a knot of tension throughout the body.'

I watched his fingers dance over some lettuce. Off came the apron.

'Chops ready to deep fry, I make two calls, get into something comfortable, we dine, more vino, Turkish café, perhaps, then you tell me what's doing with this big hunk.'

Opening the gate and taking the dog away he came back to a room just outside and was soon on the phone.

'*Gizmo*, go to the sunparlor!'

I went over and looked in. On work table along open window stood four torsos in rank with male organs thrust out like fascist salute. Keeping the wall to my back, I moved to the gate, edging an eye into the room. *Ayy! Au natural* he was to open window, phone to ear and horselike haunch to breeze.

243

Reaching to a gold dashiki spread out on the bed before him his buttocks split deep. What was in mind here I did not want to find out. Retracing my steps to the back door, it would not budge. It took a skeleton key, with no key there.

'*Gizmo*, you okay?'

'*Yes!*'

Tiptoing back to the parlor I moved the torsos aside and got up on my knees on the table. Nudging the window higher I looked down on a ledge between the second and first floor, such footpaths built in old Chicago buildings for firemen. It ran to wood stairwell behind the building. Turning on all fours I crawled out backward, my shoes scraping down to the ledge. A drop of eight nine feet to concrete walk, I did not think I could survive it landing backward on one leg. I would split my head open. Instead I palmed rough wall, sidestepping within reach of a stair rail off my right hip, not an easy grab slanting down and away. Bending at the knees what little I could, an inch no more, I pushed myself backward, twisting in mid air. *Aagh!* My jaws clapped together on wood rail. Holding on for dear life I got a knee up and chinned myself up and over. Bellying across I drummed down the stairs and covered ground.

Swerving into a rundown gas station, not the type with a restroom, I went round back and relieved myself, moaning in thanks. Rarely I bought myself a soda but slugged a cold one now like never before. A scruffy attendant – in hard need of money to be working there – was locked up with cigarettes and prophylactics. Pushing him $2 for gas I returned to my pony, passing a smart sister in heels bent over a new vehicle. Taking another pull I was Gizmo not myself.

'Baby, you need somebody to pump yo' gas!'

As she turned her eyes, out swung a bearded Negro coming straight at me. Meaning to get back into the pony instead I hit the street on the run. Snorting at my heels he strove to overtake me. Reaching strides that almost sent me sprawling, I pulled away but not before a keening '*Punk-motherfucker!*' followed me into an alley where I took cover.

Neighborhood no good, much less the alley, I was not rash. In good time I stole back to my pony. Shins shanks, my very scrotum, trembled at what I beheld. Doors bashed, tires punctured, windshield caved in by a trash barrel, the top all but torn away, I fell on my knees making circles on the panels with both hands. The attendant come up behind I turned like a mourner from a grave.

'He destroyed my vehicle.'

'Looks like it, don't it?'

Taking the valise out of the trunk I went off on foot. On a bus a young Negro asked if I just lost my best friend. I said yes. At the pool hall I got up on the abandoned shoeshine stand. Through the rear came Cully, licking an ice cream cone like a cat licks its paw.

'What's this football stuff with that stiff?'

'He's getting ready for an NFL camp.'

'*Him?* I told Hy, we yucked it up.'

'Hy ever do anything for you? You get anything out of it?'

'What I want, I pay cash. I don't mooch.'

Sarge Biltz came through the front. Having a look around he went to the counter for his cup of coffee with a fiver slid underneath, no bribe too small in Chicago.

'Was there ever an honest cop in Chicago?'

'Two . . . they starved to death.'

'Is it man's work writing parking tickets?'

He pointed to his patch. 'Sheriff's Bounty, $5 a write whenever wherever whatever. Make a job serve your intents and purposes, it don't matter what you do. Go ask Jon Peters in Hollywood. My mother's side had a confirmation, double-parking down the block. Did I go? Yeh, straight for my hack. I'm citing left and right and some buttface cuts across his lawn screaming bloody murder so I get my hat. My Italian

245

uncles are calling middle of the night. "We'll cut your fuckin' throat!" *Hey pal, no ticky no money!* I don't back off I don't get nervous I don't apologize. A bowlegged hillbilly I was stalking opens the screen door and sends out her mutt. It gets to the curb and I stomp the yippin' shit out of it. *Yip! Yip! Yip!* I drag it up the porch and say, "Next time don't send a dog to do a man's job."'

The two holdup artists, Isaac and Manuel, came through the back. Cully eased back to the wall. The Harlan County hoodlum, pretended to be impressed I was on the shoeshine stand with a valise.

'Fast-shufflin' boy, my uncle . . . leavin' town?'

'My vehicle was destroyed. Haven't seen you around.'

'My sister in Florida needed help.'

'Another sister story?'

'Her boyfriend puts her in a trailer park and goes to work for Ford, gettin' in with the boys, spendin' his check on dancers and 976 calls, leavin' her and the baby to themselves. (He glanced back at Cully at the wall.) So I call. He's gettin' *oriented* he says. Pretty soon strippers are stoppin' by and one night he has the audacity to bring around a black whore. Time for a chat.'

'Do any good?'

'He's a home-gettin' motherfucker now, he can't wait to get home. Whistle blows, *Whooo!!* He's out like a shot. He loves his little trailer now.'

He turned an eye back again. 'Hope nobody's listenin'.'

Cully slipped away. I looked over at the Mexican, Manuel, leaning against a pool table.

'You have a sister, too?'

'I have a brother who's very effeminate but no sister.'

I shrugged in sympathy.

'Want some work?' asked Isaac.'

'I was brought up not to rob and steal.'

'He who steals from a thief is no thief. You'll find that in the old Bible . . . Jews, smart ones.'

I did not recall having seen it but went to their vehicle, put the valise in the trunk and took them down US1 like the first time. We started out in high gusts but two hours south the fields were silent. I would have turned on the radio but it was their vehicle.

'24 up next.'

'It goes to Indiana.'

'What's the difference?'

Swinging left I pulled over. Isaac got out and changed plates.

Passing a long motor court all by itself out there I turned off to broken road with an old closed-up filling station ahead. Manuel swung a sledgehammer from the trunk across a trench and jumped after it. Issac pointed me on a quarter mile to paved road, the back way out. Returned to the station I pulled up alongside an old coupe under a tree, facing a side of the court.

'There's prostitution here?'

'Car dealers, Indiana hicks.'

I did not see Manuel about but a strapper six-four in a suede jacket came out of a room with a young brunette half his age and size. Tall and square-jawed like he might be local authority his pate gleamed in overhead light. Isaac leaned up to my ear.

'Baldheaded sonuvabitch got his head buffed.'

A small pick-up braked in the court drive. A delivery boy brought take-out to a room to the right of us. The door come open, Manuel from out of nowhere went by glancing in. Isaac rested a hand on my shoulder.

'You okay?'

'I could pee bad.'

'In that case . . . take a long one.'

Behind a tree I emptied my bladder and got back in.

247

He leaned up again.

'Keep your eyes on me. I wave over my head, pull out and roll backward to us, facing there.'

He pointed to the back way out.

'You'll hold we cut it close?'

'I'll hold.'

Tapped on the shoulder I looked down at a bone handle straight razor a type I knew from DeCarlo's. The blade came half out under my chin.

'We'll find you.'

'I *wouldn't* run!'

Taking a sawn gun from the trunk he jumped the trench, coming up behind Manuel stooped between vehicles with the sledgehammer. A nudge got him going for the door.

BOOM!

My eyes, buttocks and feet jumped at once. The door flew in, Manuel with it. Behind him Isaac kept a leg in a leg out. A door over a couple jumped out of bed and were looking out. My right leg shaking I got out from behind the wheel. Isaac's shout over my head sent me back in. Pulling out in reverse I rolled back in line with the smashed door.

Five six men were face down around a turned over table. Snatching up cash and personal articles, Manuel razored their pants for anything strapped to a leg. Two motel men came jogging from the front. Isaac stepped out into the drive and they came to a stop.

Out came Manuel swinging a sack. Bumping through parked vehicles he jumped the trench with Isaac behind him. Scrambling through weeds they got in slamming doors. I stepped on the gas and sped down the track. Turning onto paved road my right foot went numb and slipped off the pedal. Managing a stop before swerving aside I got out barely holding on. Isaac jumped by me to the wheel leaving a door open. Pulling myself into the back, the door slammed on my leg as we got away. I twisted up on my side trying to breathe

the cramp out. Hearing something coming I raised my head and looked out the rear.

'A car's behind us with no headlights!'

Manuel turned over his shoulder.

'A dumb hick,' said Isaac in the mirror.

Keeping its distance, if not a civilian vehicle it would make its move before we got out of Indiana. Back forth my eyes went until we crossed the line. Pulled over Manuel got out and changed plates, sending two flying.

The wind right we got back at one coming to 14th Avenue. Turned into an alley I limped after them into a dive with a bricked up front. A Greek behind the bar dealt with thieves. We went to a booth. Manuel shook out a sack of cash wallets bracelets wristwatches and a short revolver. A Chicago geezer with two bottom teeth like a possum came with a pint of Canadian Club, club soda and Dixie cups, nearly tipping them over. Manuel put down a five. He stood there like he could use a tip. Eyeing his cap Isaac gave him one.

'Stick with the Cubs, oldtimer. They'll make it someday.'

He slumped away, and Isaac turned over his shoulder.

'You won't be around, but they'll make it someday.'

Looking over wristwatches he threw one on the floor. Giving a second look he handed me one. I pushed it back. Flashing a deputy sheriff's badge in a wallet he caught my arm.

'You're under arrest for collusion collaboration corruption – *Lord* knows what else.'

Money in order Isaac shooed off a few hundreds and fifties I did not count. Wallets bracelets wristwatches sold to the Greek they drove me back behind the pool hall. Swinging out the valise I walked to the coffee shop on the next corner, counting $500 in the toilet. A quarter to three, the pool hall opened at six. Including $300 of my own money I wondered if Cabe might take $800 for the voucher and camp pass. Yukon would be on his way after all.

There at first light I thought better than to offer my last dollar? Obviously Cabe liked money. If he would take eight hundred he might take five over nothing at all. He'd made the simple proposition I brought him a task at every turn. Because of him I lost my vehicle.

An eye to the door I nodded off. Looking up I saw him going to the back. Following to the toilet I showed him $500.

'It's all I could come up with.'

Giving the Slavic curse *Shakreft* he snapped three hundreds and four fiftys between his thick fingers. A four-hundred-pounder named Wally waddled to the stall for his morning dump.

'*Git*,' advised Abe.

We went to an Olds out front. From an envelope with a Houston Oiler logo he took a United Airlines voucher and a camp pass.

'They'll sleep him over and work him out. Get him to O'hare by one?'

'He'll be there.'

'They'll be waiting for him with an Oiler sign.'

'How will we know if they sign him?'

'I'll know. Get him a sport jacket, slacks and shoes. You don't have much time.'

'A white shirt and necktie won't do?'

'Don't put him on a plane with his boots like a hick. Go to High & Wide, tell Sy I sent you.'

By now I knew 'Tell him I sent you' in Chicago meant nearly nothing.

'Cut his hair,' he added.

Taking the valise I took a bus out to 74th and came in on him asleep. Barechested he sat up and pulled on what he wore every day. I showed him the United Airlines voucher and camp pass with logo. He leaned into light.

'You'll be a Houston Oiler. You're done here.'

Taking a toothbrush and salt shaker from under the bed he went out to the privy under the stairs. Returned he stared at the pass and voucher in my hand. All he had in a denim sack we took out to a bus to 55th, walking into High & Wide, known for TV advertisement featuring Chicago athletes as tall as seven foot. Sy stood behind the counter in the same confident way Mel used to and like Mel did not look like a badhearted man. He gave Yukon a look. I put down the valise.

'Cabe Nebo sent us. He played for the Steelers and Eagles.'

'Sure.'

'Yukon here is going to Houston Oilers camp today.' I presented voucher and pass. 'He needs a blazer slacks shoes. Have you a combination that comes to a few hundred?'

'Blazers start $250.'

'You have a discount rack?'

'No rack.'

A husky college boy intruded so boldly I took him for Sy's son.

'He's on wrestling.'

'He's through wrestling. He's going to an NFL camp.'

'*NFL!* He's a stiff. He never wins. Anybody could take him.'

'It's not real,' I said.

'Why would a dude let a smaller dude mess him over if he can't do it for real? It's a show but the tougher guy in real life wins. He never beats anybody. I saw him picking up bottles. I'd wrestle him.'

'He'd snap you like a saltine.' I turned to Sy. 'You're a Jewish fellow, am I right?'

His eyes seemed to agree.

'I'm from Louisville. I don't know if you heard of Savile Row, all Jewish men. You looked sharp you went there, you looked like a farmer going to church you didn't –

that was the demarcation. Those Jews saw good material, a good bet, they put money down. They had a word – *pinoosa*. For *pinoosa* you put your money down or you were nobody. Give us a break. Take three hundred down. When Yukon comes back he'll do a commercial. You'll get your *pinoosa* twice over. He'll make the Oilers.'

Smiling like a sporting man going against his instincts he came around the counter and called his tailor Nate. I half expected a Nate I once knew.

Yukon was fitted with a chestnut sport jacket, bay pants and brogues. The jacket and pants fit a seven-foot man. We sat while the legs were shortened. Yukon put on a white shirt like a bed sheet, then the pants jacket and shoes. Sy stood him against the wall and took pictures. Dungarees boots and lumberjack in the rucksack, we stepped out twenty after eleven.

'One last thing . . . a haircut.'

'No way.'

'You can't go looking like a wild man. We have to get it cut.'

'*We*?' He looked around wanting to walk away.

'Just to the neck.'

Downstreet a Filipino sized him up and started chopping with a straight razor. When he stood up I was sure the Oilers would sign him on sight.

A bus to the underground, a train to the end of the line, an escalator to O'hare terminals, we rose like to a new world. Adults and children stood still at Yukon with his rucksack as though they had never seen such a sight. The clerk at the counter who saw the world stared. Inspecting the voucher he printed a ticket and said to take it easy. No head unturned, youngsters came closer. He took nothing from it, his eyes those of a comic-book soldier going into combat thinking he won't come back. I tugged his sleeve.

'I read that many of America's great soldiers were scared going into battle. Once shooting started they knew what they had to do. Morrow the hitting starts, you'll know. As long you make a go of it, two years three four, you'll have a place you belong and teammates to stand by.'

His eyes unchanged, I went to a pay phone and called Jackson at the tavern.

'I have him at O'hare, he's going.'

'Roye Matzak helped?'

'I paid Cabe $500 and got a Houston Oilers camp pass.'

'*Oilers!* My team! You pulled it off, little brother.'

'I have him in a new jacket and brogues but he looks shook. Is there parting advice?'

He spoke some thought. Stopping him I got pen and paper from a counter, asked he go slower and wrote every word.

'I have it!'

'Hold brave clean thoughts, little brother!'

Travelers told to board I went along with Yukon, reading Jackson's words aloud.

'Look 'em in the eye and keep your answers short. *"Thanks! Good to be here!"* Don't *yes-sir no-sir* anybody. That's for hicks and Texas buttholes. Don't be impressed with what newcomers say. They went to college and did things unknown to you. It means nothing once you get on grass. Strength and saavy, single combat. You've been doing fifteen twenty a day. Nobody is as ready as you. Make no friends, go easy on no one. Whoever they put in front of you, *turn* him out. They see that in you they'll count you in!'

I took out my wallet and handed him a twenty, leaving myself $12.

'We'll work out a schedule for my share. You'll have a lot coming at you. Nothing's left here for me. You have too much to handle I can come help, read the fine print, manage the money, be your fiduciary so to speak.'

253

He still wouldn't look at me.

'They'll be waiting with a sign, but they'll probably recognize you.'

I laughed at what I said. He showed the pass and went through the gate. I stood a moment like an Israelite leaving Egypt – only so can I describe it – a block of wet clay and straw fallen from my thin shoulders.

Taking the valise I saw a Polynesian style lounge the other way. Bartender and waitress there but no customers, I sat down in back. She called over.

'What'll you have?'

'A tall Tom Collins with a cherry or two.'

She brought the drink, 'Three-seventy-five.'

Did I ever think I would pay $4 for a drink? I looked across the bar at a TV sports show. A player's agent spoke of his client's new contract as though it was most important news. In a week or two or three I could very well be part of this artificial world myself.

I imagined Charlene in humble Louisville happening upon me on TV as Yukon's agent. Shocked she'd be. DiJi and I were too much a mismatch, and with Mammy and Theo in the way we had no chance to pull it off.

Walking like never before, like my leg had straightened on its own, almost to a trot, I stopped in my tracks at Yukon at the boarding counter dickering with the clerk. A second attendant arrived backing up company policy.

'We can't switch voucher destinations.'

'You can't get me somewhere else?'

Tapped on a shoulder he looked behind him.

'Why aren't you on board?'

His breathing stopped, he could not answer. I appealed to the attendant. 'Has the plane gone?'

'No.'

'Let him back on, he's a football player, he's expected in Houston today.'

Yukon turned away.

'It's there for you, you're invited, they're waiting.'

'Not for me,' he breathed sitting down.

'Not for *you!* I gave Cabe $500 for the voucher. I paid for the jacket and pants. You led me on.'

'You wanted to hang on me.'

'Hang on you? I wanted to be a brother to you. I would have taken off my pants and shoes to give to you. You never even looked me in the eye.'

He would not reply.

'You want to be a phony all your life? That's all you see for yourself, a stooge for Hy Speed and gyps like him? Don't you see what you're passing up? We'll go to a truck stop and find a way there.'

He wanted to get away from me but where could he go with $20 in his pocket – not even back to his hovel? What use, it was undone? I made for the escalator. Followed I read his eyes – he wanted advice. It was simple enough: go back to sleeping in the bus and work your way up with Hy. Else I saw little better than casual labor or the car wash.

On the train he sat by himself. Getting off I went up on the street, crossing over to catch the Cermak bus. He stayed at the curb. I knew what he was going to do, loiter downtown in coffee shops laying his head on counter tops.

'You gonna be at the card?' he called over.

'I got nowhere else to go.'

Come to Cermak I walked up Adams Road wondering if Cabe might refund $250 so I could pay rent and restore some occupancy to the patch.'

Next morning I was at the pool hall. Head hung I looked up at him standing over me.

'You got him off?'

My eyes clenched.

'He wouldn't go.'

'What?'

'He got on and off.'

'Why?'

'Not for him he said.'

I couldn't look him in the eye.

'He *would'na* made it.'

'After what you saw?'

'What'd I see, a *farce?* I went against old saavy: too raw, out-of-nowhere, he wouldn't even talk.'

'Can I ask something, Cabe?'

'Ask.'

'I need money to get back on my feet. Would you refund half?'

'Absolutely not! I went out on a limb for this guy. They're gonna wonder if I'm worth listening to – you want money back?'

He did not even have his cup of coffee. I sat around most of the day wondering if I deserved to buy myself a red hot, no more in mind than that. Six-thirty I crossed to the bus stop. Getting to the armory I came upon black and red *Rasslin' Flash* semi-trailor and matching bus. I had read about *Rasslin' Flash* in a finance magazine. Young enterpriser Jerry Bernstein followed through on his idea that with baseball football basketball highlights becomming nightly TV staple he could do the same with a wrestling weekly. Wrestling rabble had only their local promotion and the Saturday night show from New York. Scores of promotions around, mainly South and West, featured regional wrestlers who had developed clever characters and gimmicks. Paying matchmakers a promotional spot for the venue, and wrestlers $100 each for filming, he produced a syndicated show that according to him was 'hauling in like nobody's business.' You had to hand it to him but he did not start with nothing like I always did. It took money for cameras crew and carry.

I followed cable down to the arena where *Rasslin' Flash* had built a platform. Unlike seasoned Channel 4 employees this crew was young and loud. Like for any sizable event Chicago Yellow Jackets were hired to keep order, local toughs who worked venues and had a reputation for getting rough with you. Hy Speed cane down the ramp in step with Jerry Bernstein, a stocky hustler with razor cut hair. By the tone of conversation he was more brash than Hy.

I repaired to the rear. Back in his old things Yukon sat down near me. Hy Speed came by.

'Where were you two yesterday, you riding with me or not? I get calls from all over begging a look. You got better get out! Go play with yourselves. Go to the sticks, see what those hicks in Kentucky and Indiana pay. Don't show up again, you're through, both of you.'

'Who's he with?' he yelled to Cully in the office.

'Rick McDude, third up.'

'Get this stiff and him over with first. I needed this with *Rasslin' Flash* here.'

It would be a wrong match. Rick McDude was the most particular marquee, expecting jobbers to be keen on all he was wont to do. Shaking his mane, twitching his chest, moody as usual, told he was first up he snapped back, 'This is goddam unprofessional!'

On with his tights he pointed Yukon out the double doors and demonstrated twisting holds and breakouts. I stood by wondering how he expected a crude character like Yukon to get it. Coming down the corridor the Sammos turned into the rear but not before Sonny and Yukon locked eyes.

There was a stir in the arena. Hy and Jerry Bernstein center ring threw rubber figurines to incomming rabble. Two cameramen positioned themselves outside the ropes, angled opposite of one another to capture action front and rear or 'double inverted' as Jerry Bernstein told Hy.

The arena near full Red Canyon called out in his booming Southern man voice to give an ol' back home welcome to *Rasslin' Flash*. He might have been the phoniest part of the show for I had long got it that so-called Southern Hospitality from the established and well-to-do was preferential, self-negotiated and rarely from kindness. Kindness, if any, came from the poor.

I led Yukon into the ring. A scrawny bible thumper stole in ahead of us to harangue the rabble, who turned on him. Yellow Jackets came. Not going along he was taken out by his feet and throat. Rabble howled *Hypocrite!* though I was sure they didn't know what it meant. I looked around at them, slavering licking their lips, the sameness of their faces – inexcusable uneducated existence in a land that offers schooling and enlightenments like a mother coaxes a child to eat from a spoon. They would waste away from stupidity, no more. I stood there with a notion I would have hardly thought possible of me. I knew of enforced sterilization from my reading, disturbed by such a thing, yet asked myself looking around, 'What would be lost? *What* for all practical purposes would America as a people as a land lose to rid themselves of this waste?'

Lights dimming at guitar squeals over loudspeakers, Rick McDude danced down the ramp shaking his mane. Loping to the ring he sprang through the ropes. I didn't fear him like I feared other marquees who I took for roughhousers. Him I saw as having been a touchy youth who discovered weightlifting, building a large upper half through self-love but retaining skinny legs he hid in tights.

From the bell it was like two starting to dance, one wanting to kick up his heels, the other with no notion where to put his feet. Usually Yukon bullied a marquee into a corner and let him have it but Rick McDude wanted to start with a reverse kick out. Yukon too new to provide the chute, it looked like Rick McDude bounced off a wall. The next move no better, rabble began to grumble. I slammed my hands on the mat and swiped at Rick McDude's heels but it was pointless against the ineptitude above. They tripped over one another and even the dullest rabble laughed. Hy Speed came down the ramp slicing a finger across his throat.

Taking Yukon's arm Rick McDude ran him corner to corner. Now Yukon knew what to do, hitting the posts so that they shook. Rick McDude climbed his back, forced him down to his knees and turned him over for the easy pin. Rabble going '*Lame lame lame!*' he bounced on his toes, pointing two fingers in victory. Yukon sagged down the stoop and I followed him to the rear. Kicking back in the office, Romeo and I exchanged looks the way Sonny and Yukon had. Handsome and tanned with a million-dollar smile he was not muscled-up like Sonny and other marquees. It looked he could put on a suit and do well for himself but those gyp eyes of his wouldn't hold for it. His gain needed someone or other's loss, his grin their harm.

A circuit wrestler with a boy seven or eight loosened up in a red satin jacket with U.S. Marine campaign patches. The boy carried a stack of glossy photos of his father in grappler pose. There was polish in the Marine's footwork. Looking for somebody to gab with he held out his hand.

'Marion Morris.'

'Gizmo.'

'You play a joker?'

'That says it,' I agreed.

The little guy stood behind his father, his eyes brave little Johnny Shiloh's in library picture books.

'Your boy travels with you?'

'Nine months a year I read with him. What use of school, so he'll learn to light and smoke dope? His mother makes a life of prostitution at the Mustang Ranch out in Nevada. Her no-good sister put her up to it. She gets Ezekiel here three months. Hired some stiff prick: "Didn't *you*. . . ? Isn't it *true*. . . ?" Thought he had me until he confuses hisself. "Excuse me," I ask "didn't you just say left was right and right was wrong?"'

259

'You want to be a Marine, too?' I asked his little guy.

That got a sure nod.

'He'll go twenty, not call it at ten like me. Hold rank, know what's expected of you, what to expect of others. No fake-outs where a lawyer can take a man's son even if his mother is a . . . Couldn't ask for better, sleeps in the wagon, sets up a little stand and sells my pictue for a dollar.'

He peeked around his father.

'Smile, c'mon, smile,' he said to Yukon.

For the only time I saw something turn in his eyes.

'Shake hands with him, Ezekiel,' the marine said.

He came forward, his father's pictures tucked to his chest with twisted little fingers and a limp arm. I'd have given an eye not to see it. Yukon shook his hand.

'How are things on the road?' I asked the Marine.

'Hurtin', I learned it, it was switch and switch back, trick or treat, light on the feet. Now who barks loudest makes the rules. I broke in they'd get booed just the way they walk to the ring. Public turning on common decency, don't know right from wrong. Give 'em blood. That's all they want. Old pros steppin'over the line, turnin' bloodthirsty. Used to be some brotherhood. Run-through yesterday, Sammo in there acted like he was sparing me the time.'

'He'll try to choke you.'

'He wants to get rough he'll get a mouthful. I was a hand to hand instructor in the Corps. Up in Milwaukee that wrinkled old goat Bull Swensen got slaphappy. Lams me with a left, another with the right. I cuffed him right back. Ask Ezekiel here. Old goat had me play a heel in Marine get-up. Teamed me with Farouk the Terrorist like I was a traitor to my country.'

Cully came with clipboard. 'Marion the Marine.'

To *Anchors Aweigh* I followed him and Ezekiel through the corridor and down the ramp. Ducking through the ropes he proudly shook hands with Terry Donley, took off his red jacket and handed it down to Ezekiel who folded it like a flag. Pawing the canvas with his feet he was good to go. Terry Donley gave the call with only Marion in the ring.

'Next fall, one hour time limit, in blue corner at a slippery 220, from Owensboro, Kentucky, Marion the Marine.'

Rabble hooted him despite the Marine get-up. To *Jimmy Crack Corn* Sonny and Romeo did a jig coming into the ring, Romeo sporting his war club and gyp grin. Terry Donley swung around.

'In red corner, at 260 pounds, accompanied by brother Romeo, half of the World Tag Team Champions, the Mako Shark, Sonny Sammo.'

Crabwalking belly up Sonny thrilled the rabble with his uncivilized antics. At the bell they locked up. Sonny forced him into the ropes and broke clean. Marion swiped him with the back of his hand. Sonny dropped to his knees holding his throat. Marion charged falling into his trap. Sonny rammed both shoulders into his hips, drove him against a ringpost and backpedaled to the opposite corner. Among the crowd one blew a horn and from across the ring Sonny scampered across doubling Marion over.

Coming up from behind Hy took me to the rear and tore into me and Yukon both.

'The tape stinks. Jerry Bernstein says he never saw anything that bad. You're through, both of you. Come back when you know something, I'm wasting no more time on you.'

He slammed the office door behind him, leaving me wondering if we would be paid the $100 each. I had $6 left in my wallet. The arena grew louder with Sonny hurtling into Marion on the ropes. As he sagged Romeo popped up from the deck and jabbed him from behind with the balsa club, sending him to his knees. Twisting an arm behind him Sonny got him up on tiptoes and turned him in a circle, prodding him to salute the house.

'Salute, *brudda*, snap one off!'

Not going along he was kicked in the buttocks.

'Snap one off, brudda!'

A Marine will wrench a joint to throw one last punch. Marion swung a fist over his shoulder and Sonny swept a leg out from under him.

'Watch you doin', old man? You wanna show me up?'

Marion stuck his head through the ropes for refuge but out of nowhere Romeo with his devilish Jack-in-the-box trickery highbridged him with his club. Slashed across the nose Marion tried to clear his eyes.

Coming ringside Ezekiel tried to get up to him but was shooed away. Turning for help he ran to the bell table.

'My dad's bleeding.'

Red Canyon waved to Yellow Jackets to come take him. Ezekiel ran up the ramp and down the corridor to the rear, to Jackanapes L'l All-America Kilowatts Bullseye and others.

'My dad's bleeding, please help him?'

No one moved an inch. Come to Yukon and me he took my sleeve.

'Help my dad?'

Jobbers behind us turned away.

'You comin'?' I said to Yukon.

He said nothing and I hopped after Ezekiel through the corridor and down to ringside to his father on all fours, blood running down over his mouth and chin and Sonny's foot on his rump.

The referee deaf to me I sensed Romeo afoot. Nudging Ezekiel away I slipped dybuk out from under my jacket. Timing him by the rabble's tittering I felt him almost at my neck, a foot or two away. Swinging around I let fly across his mug. *Aagh!* He bent away bowing to the waist to the rabble.

Three more he took over the back of the neck until he was on his knees.

Dealing out blows in a fight you have no hope to win, a sense of swift retaliation comes of its own. From behind I was pulled up to the ropes by my collar and smacked on the back of the head. Hanging there chin to chest, making no sound nor letting go of dybuk, I was pulled in and stomped flat by Sonny's bare feet, each thud coming heavier. Romeo climbed up into the ring. *'Let me!'* he whined. Balled up in the corner I covered my head for there seemed to be no hope. *Hoomph! Hoomph!* Jolts reverberated through my skull. My ears clogged, eyes gone into half-light, a few more would see me done. Shouldering one another to zero in Sonny swiped Romeo aside and reared back once and for all. I did not need to look, bracing for the jolt.

Djinn! The ring shook like a yard of bricks hit down on the other end. Sonny came down on me all right – backward and limp – followed by a scream like a man split apart at the groin. My eyes turned up. It was Yukon Kid. Lifting Romeo upside down by the cast, he swung him overhead like a door torn off the hinges and slammed him down on Sonny and me. *Graagh!* My chin drubbed the mat. Half asphyxiated I nosed for air.

Not letting go Yukon swung him back up and down on us like a man beating a carpet. At my last gasp I twisted out from underneath, paddling under the ropes and dropping to the deck. At Romeo's shrieks the referee fled, no longer wanting witness here. Pulling myself to my feet I joined in from the deck, cracking dybuk down on Sonny and Romeo's heads as Yukon slammed them together. Their jaws clacking like puppets, there was not enough consciousness between them to blink an eye.

Rabble openmouthed, Hy Speed called on Yellow Jackets to break this up. Storming the ring they fell on Yukon to restore order. Letting Romeo drop he was bulled into a corner, all in a wedge against him. Fighting for room he bucked his shoulders off the ropes but they were too many. When he wouldn't hold still those on the flanks threw fists. Unflinching he stood alone against them. Up from his knees Marion the Marine pitched into them with one arm. If he could take courage so would I. Climbing the stoop I pranced in on one leg and laid onto heads, heedless at what would befall me now. A Yellow Jacket turned on me, pulling my collar, clawing at my neck from his knees. I gave back fivefold, flailing, gaining height as I beat him for the fight was now to our end or theirs. He took five six and disgorged a groan begging no more. We were to grips with them fighting hand to hand, each man for his own life. At a sensation like there was wind behind us Marion and I beat down two more. Yukon got a grip into the rest, seesawing them. Those in close swung side to side, those behind hung on heaving, *'Go for his legs!'* On a heave of his own Yukon's right hand broke through. Punching point-blank his blows split them apart. Jaws snapped skyward, teeth flew. Those who could ran, reeling over the fallen. Others motionless on the mat saw their chance and scrambled out under the ropes. Marquees were called to the rescue.

Jackanapes Bullseye L'l All-America Rick McDude Kilowatts 8-Ball Colonel Petan Hiram Schnapps Cleeton Flowers Muskrat Joe YMCA Kid Up'n'Up Barry and regrouped Yellow Jackets came like a flying wedge. Leading the charge Hy waved them in. They stormed the ring expecting the scene to deliver them but Yukon Marion and I met them with fists kicks dybuk, laying them low. Hiram Schnapps, strongest of the marquees, was coldcocked. Muscular 8-Ball caught the next and capsized. Jackanapes flew heels over buttocks. Bullseye was cut down, Kilowatts upended nearby. Flattened on his face Petan rose to his knees, grappling in the gore of his mouth for his teeth. From but a ricochet on hollow jaw L'll All-America buckled in the knees, then Up'n'Up Barry collapsed from a mere swipe. Cleeton Flowers and YMCA Kid tried climbing Yukon on both sides only to be flung from opposite hands, biting mat and rope. Kid came again to his woe. Caught by the throat he choked until his mouth twisted inside out. The coward Rick McDude slid out to safety and ran. Gentle Barry followed. Gripping a hand to his throat Cleeton Flowers threw himself over the side with no thought as to where his head would land.

Trading blow for blow, flinging back at them two steps to one we retook the ring. I fell on those falling back on me, reaping head neck haunch. There was no holding me. *Yagh! Yagh! Yagh!* I sang as they flopped like fish before me. I searched out L'l All America. On his knees whistling through his nose, he held out a hand. I savaged him. Those left whisked themselves under the ropes and fled without shame from *Rasslin' Flash* cameras. Looking for anybody left, Yukon swung around at the two camera operators, who lept to the deck only to be collared and excoriated by Jerry Bernstein to get back in place. Running about Hy needed only to see the look on his face to realize what went wrong went right. The tape would be sold to every podunk station with the price of a license.

Top half of the rabble pushing down on the rest, what was left of Yellow Jackets were around Hy. Yukon Marion I had cleared the ring. In a gasp I called to anybody who still wanted some to come get it. There were no takers. Slipping through the ropes Hy offered up the championship belts from a demeaning crouch. Terry Donley followed with the mic. The old gentleman's call shook.

'There are crowns won without sanction in battle so perilous they can't be denied. We were witness today. Let us proclaim new World Tag Team Champions – Marion the Marine and Yukon Kid of the North Woods.'

Rabble squealing like slopped swine, Yukon and Marion got on the belts. *Anchors Aweigh* carried us all up the ramp and down the corridor to the rear. Blocked by Hy's arm at the door, his eyes were fierce.

'Off limits, *Rasslin' Flash* is going to interview.'

'I'm Yukon's manager, I have a contract with him.'

'Mine overrides yours.'

'I'll get a lawyer.'

'*Get* a lawyer!' he spit. 'Know why I'm not scared? I *am* a goddam lawyer! *Try me! Just try me!* Nobody fucks with me and gets away with it.'

I tried to get under his arm.

'*Yukon*! He won't let me in.'

Only Ezekiel held out his hand, Yukon turned his back.

Rick McDude and Up'n'Up Barry came yelling they had been led to slaughter. Yes, agreed Hy, something had gone wrong.

'That cripple bastard, Gizmo, started this. Get him!'

I did not wait around for what might be planned for me in the lot.

I got back to the patch, the square-jawed mongrel waiting at the gate. I fixed him a meal, went inside and lay down wondering where to turn. Laden with every jolt of foot and fist come upon me, it was morn before I knew it. I woke sorebacked, paining down the sides, *whirrrr* like that of a lathe in both ears. Thankful my ribs weren't cracked – for I knew the pain – I pulled on pants and shoes to go out and feed Square-jaw. Fixing something inside for myself I went back to bed and rose midnoon shivering like it was January not July. Washing up best I could – hardly able to reach around – I walked Square-jaw down Adams Road to a wrecking yard. The operator said the place would turn him gray as mud. He gave a number to call his sister who was looking for a strong dog.

Returned to the trailer I packed everything I could in the valise and took out. Eve we got to a trucker's café over the Indiana line dead on our feet. I tethered him to a post. Half a dozen drivers were at the counter, men with ways of the road in their manner. Two Highway Patrolmen sat over a meal.

'Anybody heading south want company? I have a dog.'

A trucker went to the jukebox and played one from the 50s, a song before rock 'n' roll.

'Who's that? I'll take you.'

'Eddie Fisher, one of my favorite entertainers, and I hear his daughter is a hell of an actress.'

'Who else you like?'

'Don't forget Tony Bennett. He left his heart in San Francisco.'

I called over to the patrolmen.

'Please put out an APB on Tony Bennett's heart. California, it's a long state, ain't it?'

They nodded.

'You're welcome . . . Oh, I got that ass backwards. I should have said thanks. You two are officers and gentlemen. . . .'

Back in Louisville I remembered my way. First I went to good ground, eight years since I stood over Granme, and told her I was okay. A few recognized me here and there but had little to say. I took several jobs downtown to get my bearing, then picked up on Savile Row selling suits. Mel's old store was subdivided by three, one a suit store run by a Greek who told me Mel had three super stores going in Miami, raking in cocaine money pumped into the economy there. He also heard Mel's brother Jerry got into the nightclub business with partners and was doing better than Mel. I was happy to know about Mel but hearing Jerry was successful did me no good.

Renting a room I bought up-to-date clothes and went early one morning to Dixie Cab, asking for Charlene. Hoping she hadn't changed much I meant to simply ask, 'Do you remember me, Daupin, your husband?' The dispatcher said she didn't know her. I went out to wait for the shift change. The first arriving had no idea who Charlene was until one said, 'You mean *Breakfast?*' I asked why he called her that and he said if you bought her breakfast she gave you a blowjob. She went to Chicago he said. I went about weeks wondering if we hadn't just missed each other – like ships in the night.

I got a job in a men's store a few doors down from Mel's selling everything from Spanish suits to Australian boots. Clientele mainly young black men I took five percent and it wasn't hard to make $40 a day. A year there I met Sonya who was down and out. She presented herself as an avid reader and I fell for that and all her other lies to get a roof over her head. It went bad from the start and ended with her outside on a Monday eve screaming I was 'sexually defunct,' and that my 'very root hairs' made her skin crawl.' I threw her few things out on the walk and had the locks changed. She went on to harass me at my work before she finally left me in peace.

Buying a car on payments, that very day I leaned over to offer a young lady at a bus stop a lift. I was unjustly arrested and it took all the money I had saved to keep me from going to jail. After that I sort of gave up on the whole thing.

Moving to the Heights which was well integrated now I got a job helping minorities prepare applications for low interest loans. Paid commission I did well until one testicle swelled up twice the size of the other. I had never been to a doctor and a co-worker said something similar had happened to his right bicep but it returned to size. Letting it go on that I awoke on a Sunday to a testicle the size of my fist. I was taken to a hospital and it was removed. I haven't felt right since.

Gin was my friend awhile but it tried to turn on me. Square-jaw passed on and he was a good companion. I grew half gray. My days untroubled two Quebec publicists sent a letter saying they would like me to come and tour the province as the Lost Dauphin. I know if you file a tax return you can probably be located – but how did they know? Loyalist Societies throughout the province would pay to see me they beseeched me but offered neither fare nor accommodations.

Morn with a free moment from work I oft crossed the street for something sweet. One day a Cadillac Seville shaking at the joints braked at my knees. Two large men inside, the driver called me to the window.

I knew his face even though it had billowed, his hair no longer red but white and cropped. He was smiling, I remembered not a one.

'You're Gizmo, right?'

'What are you doing here?'

'We're startin' a show at the Elks. We're gonna try to make it here.'

'Good luck.'

'Ever see me on television?'

'I don't watch much television.'

'I was in wrestling magazines. I was up and down the Eastern Seaboard.'

He looked me more in the eyes now than in all the time I knew him.

'I'm a paranoid schizo,' he added.

I was unsure how to reply, I did not know what it was.

'First show's Friday, come help.'

'I'm not so light on my feet these days.'

'Up here,' he tapped his head. 'Smarts.'

'Maybe.'

'You gonna be there or are you just sayin' it?'

He smiled in need, his prime gone like mine.

'I'll come.'

A car came honking and he held up a bible from the dashboard.

'*He* called me by name and I heard *His* voice.'

I got coffee and a roll and stood watching a clerk and vendor trying to get the better of one another. The women who honked came jangling her keys, asking for cigarettes and cough drops. A neatly dressed young man peered through magazines he had no intention to buy. I watched him walk through the lot each morn looking for something to pick up. Two power company guys grabbed snacks they would pay a high premium for. They were grinning, unconcerned what an armful of snacks would cost. I grinned, too.

Ahhhh . . . what was there to lament? I had been false to no one. I'd walked straight as I could on a crooked leg. I was not made strong but when there was fighting to do I went out and did it. I took up with armed robbers once but in a way they were more honorable than others who'd had me at a disadvantage. I failed in my endeavors but I'd faced only uphill, the way of one who is outmatched, that of the underdog and overcomer, and for a time – if I might charm myself a little – I was of the little-known saga of the Lost Dauphin and Yukon Kid.